Pirates

The Cursed

Shuky & Gorobei

Author: Shuky **Illustrator:** Gorobei **Translation:** Adam Marostica
This book is a translation of the original *Pirates 3* © Makaka Editions

ISBN : 978-1-952116-01-8 Library of Congress Control Number: 2020937969

Published by Van Ryder Games and printed in China. First Printing.

Find printable investigation sheets and other Graphic Novel Adventures at www.vanrydergames.com

AS YOU CAN SEE ME MATEYS, I'VE FOUND A RATHER EXPERTLY CRAFTED MAP THAT'LL LET US NAVIGATE THESE WATERS MUCH FASTER.

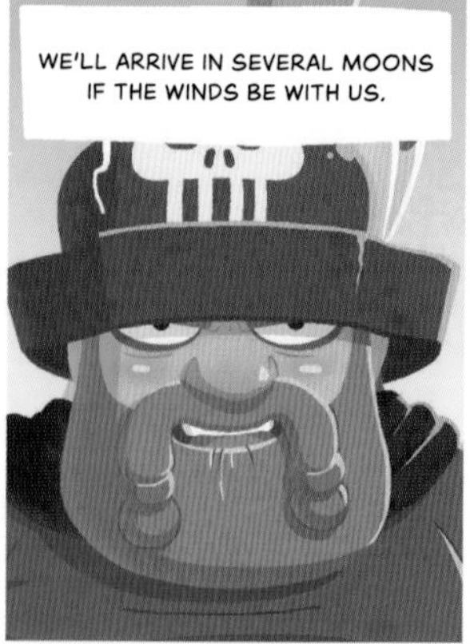
WE'LL ARRIVE IN SEVERAL MOONS IF THE WINDS BE WITH US.

WHICH MEANS, SEVERAL MOONS FROM NOW, WE'LL PILLAGE THAT BLASTED ISLAND AND PLUNDER ALL THEIR TREASURE!

NOW, EVERYONE TO YOUR POSTS, AND MAKE IT SNAPPY!

If you've finished "Pirates - The City of Skulls" and were made the captain's second in command, go to 275. Otherwise, continue to the next page.

Hop to it, you scalawags!
AND, SEVERAL MOONS LATER...

HURRY UP AND GET THAT LIFEBOAT IN THE WATER OR I'LL THROW YOU ALL IN THE BRIG, WHERE YOU AND THE RATS CAN LAZE ABOUT TOGETHER!

HA HA HA! THE PEOPLE OF THIS MUST BE TREMBLING WITH FEAR AS THEY WATCH US DRAW NEAR. THIS HAS TO BE MY FAVORITE PART OF BEING A PIRATE.
THAT AND THROWING PRISONERS INTO SHARK INFESTED WATERS.

THEY'RE RATHER WELCOMING FOR SCARED VILLAGERS!

WELCOME NOBLE ADVENTURERS! WE'VE BEEN IMPATIENTLY WAITING FOR YOUR ARRIVAL.

WHY WERE YOU WAITING FOR US? SOME SORT OF VILLAGE CARNIVAL?

COCO HERE WAS SENT TO FIND CAPABLE ADVENTURERS TO HELP US. THAT'S WHY HE CAME TO FIND YOU.
HELP YOU? SHIVER ME TIMBERS, WHAT DO YOU TAKE US FOR? BOY SCOUTS?

YOUR REPUTATION PRECEDES YOU, AS WE KNOW VERY WELL WHO YOU ARE. WE PROMISE THAT IF YOU HELP US, YOU'LL BE HANDSOMELY REWARDED.
I'M PERFECTLY CALM... NOW REMOVE THOSE RIDICULOUS DISGUISES IF YOU WANT TO CONTINUE THIS CONVERSATION.

THAT'S PRECISELY THE PROBLEM, MY FRIEND. A TERRIBLE CURSE HAS FALLEN UPON OUR ISLAND. AND NOW, WE ALL LOOK LIKE... THIS.

WE DON'T KNOW WHERE THE CURSE CAME FROM, WHICH IS WHY YOU'RE HERE. WE NEED PROPER ADVENTURERS TO HELP US!

YOUR MISSION, SHOULD YOU CHOOSE TO ACCEPT IT, WILL BE TO FIND THE SOURCE OF THE CURSE AND REVERSE ITS EFFECTS.

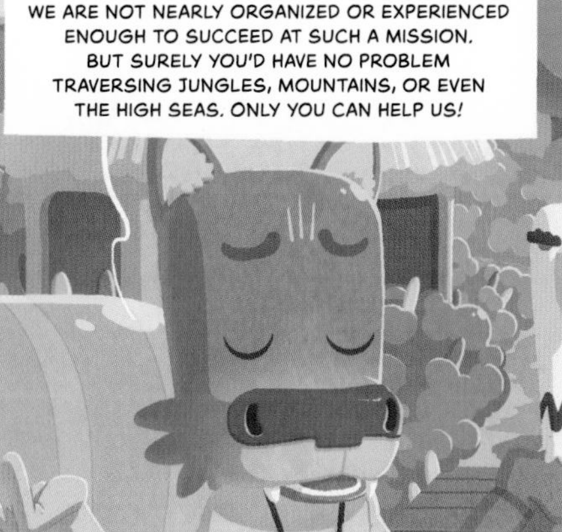
WE ARE NOT NEARLY ORGANIZED OR EXPERIENCED ENOUGH TO SUCCEED AT SUCH A MISSION. BUT SURELY YOU'D HAVE NO PROBLEM TRAVERSING JUNGLES, MOUNTAINS, OR EVEN THE HIGH SEAS. ONLY YOU CAN HELP US!

E

If you accept the mission, choose and prepare your character on the next two pages, and then review the rules on page 8. Otherwise, go to 163.

Characters

Characteristics

Strength : 8
Agility : 8
Intelligence : 8
Persuasion : 3
Intuition : 3

Characteristics

Strength : 13
Agility : 4
Intelligence : 5
Persuasion : 7
Intuition : 1

Characteristics

Strength : 4
Agility : 10
Intelligence : 13
Persuasion : 0
Intuition : 3

Characteristics

Strength : 5
Agility : 13
Intelligence : 8
Persuasion : 2
Intuition : 2

Character Sheet

Character name : ....

Characteristics :

Strength	1	2	3	4	5	6	7	8	9	10	11	12	13	14	15	16	17	18	19	20	21	22	23	24	25	26	27	28	29	30
Agility	1	2	3	4	5	6	7	8	9	10	11	12	13	14	15	16	17	18	19	20	21	22	23	24	25	26	27	28	29	30
Intelligence	1	2	3	4	5	6	7	8	9	10	11	12	13	14	15	16	17	18	19	20	21	22	23	24	25	26	27	28	29	30
Persuasion	1	2	3	4	5	6	7	8	9	10	11	12	13	14	15	16	17	18	19	20	21	22	23	24	25	26	27	28	29	30
Intuition	1	2	3	4	5	6	7	8	9	10	11	12	13	14	15	16	17	18	19	20	21	22	23	24	25	26	27	28	29	30

Collected Objects
(You may carry a number of objects equal to your Strength)

Light Objects
(Objects that don't weigh anything)

Equipment
(Objects you can wear. Clother, jewelry, etc.)

Gold Coins

Clues

Genral Notes

Resume at panel : ....

You can download this sheet and find other Graphic Novel Adventures at www.VanRyderGames.com.

Game Rules

You're about to embark on a brand new adventure! If you played the previous Pirates book, The City of Skulls, you can keep the character, including the characteristics and objects you had, previously. If you prefer, you can also start fresh by choosing on the characters on page 6. If this is your first adventure, I'd heartily encourage you to keep reading.

In Pirates your choices shape your story, and create your adventure. You can do almost anything you want, other than skip ahead and cheat of course. Any object you come across can be picked up along the way and placed in your bag, but you can't steal items that belong to someone else. However... if there is something you are allowed to steal, the panel will specifically indicate the choice to make with a number or text. You can't put things in the bag that wouldn't fit of course, so no camels, mountains, or trees! Not that any of those would really help...

You can only carry as many objects as you have strength points, and no more. That said, you can always throw away old objects to pick up new ones. Objects you wear, like jewelry and clothes or other Equipment, don't count towards your weight limit. Some other objects might "weigh nothing" and will be noted in the panel as Light Objects.

Make sure to take notes so you don't forget important clues. Check every panel for hidden objects, secret passages, and hard to spot clues. Whatever you do, don't cheat! It just ruins the surprise of different paths for the next time you play.

You'll also find puzzles throughout your adventure. Usually, the solution will form a sequence of numbers that will indicate a panel you will turn to. You'll know you've found the correct solution if it brings you to a panel with an icon at the top right that matches the one found in puzzle's panel. If there's no symbol it means you got something wrong, and you need to try again by returning to the previous panel with the puzzle.

If you're younger than 15 years of age, give your character 7 more Intelligence and 7 more Intuition.

Now, continue on to 15.

001

001

002

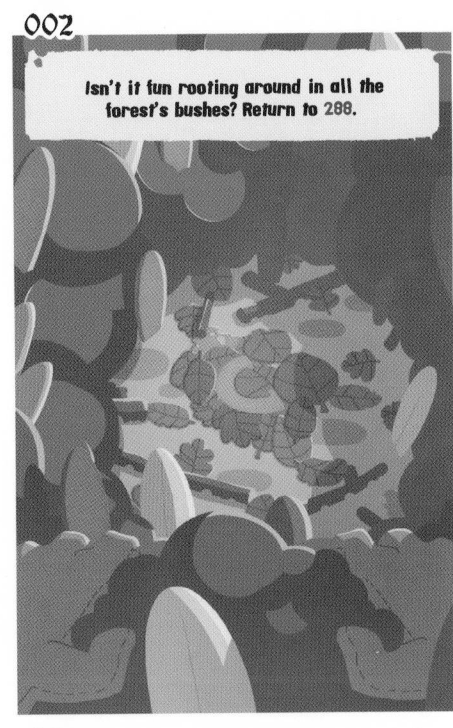

Isn't it fun rooting around in all the forest's bushes? Return to 288.

003

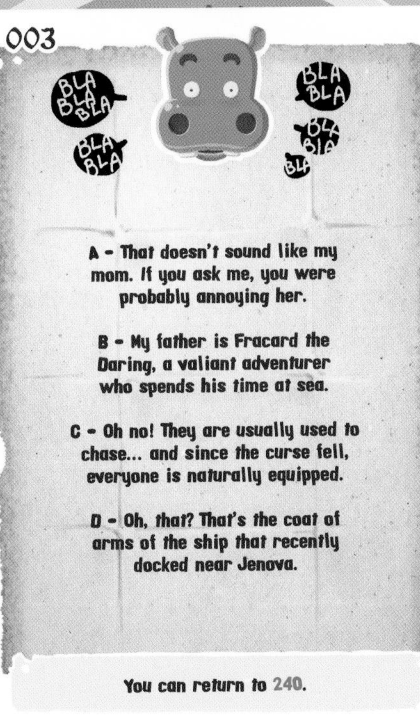

BLA BLA BLA
BLA BLA
BLA BLA
BLA BLA
BLA

A - That doesn't sound like my mom. If you ask me, you were probably annoying her.

B - My father is Fracard the Daring, a valiant adventurer who spends his time at sea.

C - Oh no! They are usually used to chase... and since the curse fell, everyone is naturally equipped.

D - Oh, that? That's the coat of arms of the ship that recently docked near Jenova.

You can return to 240.

004

There, it wasn't so hard after all, was it?
328

005

Your analytical mind and adventuring skills led you to collect these stones. They are simultaneously solid and porous, and remind you strangely of volcanic rock, which is why you decide to call them: red volcanic stones. Return to 303.

006

OH, THAT IS SO KIND OF YOU! PLEASE COME IN, INSPECTOR PIRATE, COME IN TO 294.

007

BLA BLA BLA
BLA BLA
BLA BLA
BLA BLA
BLA

A - I... I.... I love, I agree... bring on the next one! Now, let me go, if you please!

B - What are you talking about? All we did was pass by the island. We never even stopped.

C - I... I'm a sailor. I'm no cook, but I could make you some pastry, if you like.

D - The what?

After releasing the sailor, you go to 141 to take stock of the situation.

008

Marvelous discovery! In the chest, you find 50 gold pieces and a Potion of Persuasion that you can use when you wish for a temporary boost of 2 persuasion. The effect only lasts for one panel. You can return to your boat on page 2.

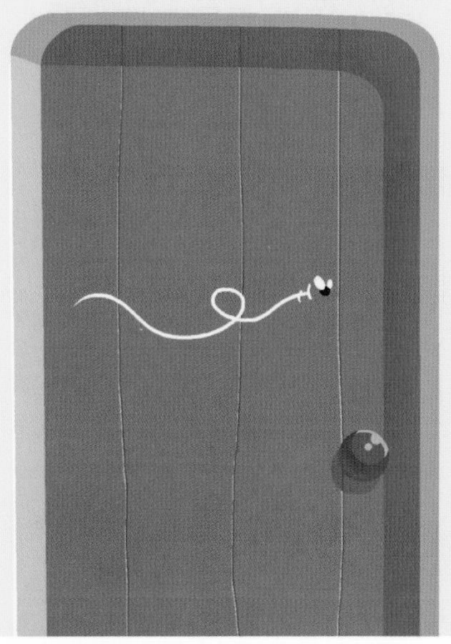
Although you knocked very loudly, no one answers. You can turn back to 119.

Is spying on your neighbors part of your mission? No, I didn't think so. Return to 72.

Old Wanosh
Ooh, goody... surely this is some sort of clue! Return to 314 when you're finished.

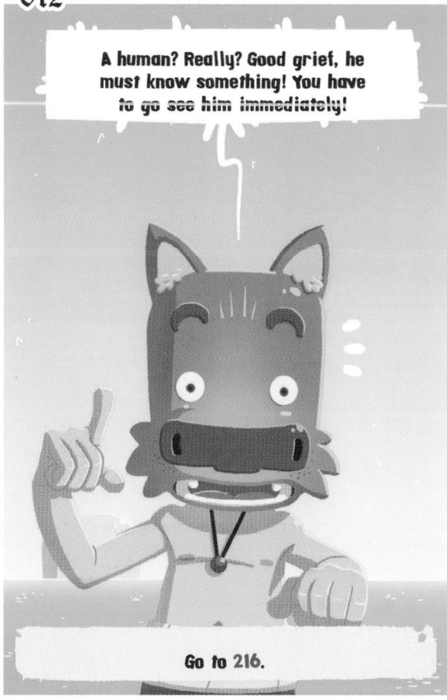
A human? Really? Good grief, he must know something! You have to go see him immediately!
Go to 216.

A real pirate would've immediately understood that it wasn't prudent to keep going... and also, between you and me, the number of the panel should've been a pretty big hint to steer clear, too. Now you're wet AND dead... restart at page 2.

014

A - I heard that a boat had anchored near Jenova island. That mean anything to you?
B - Did you see any suspicious boats shortly before the curse took hold of the island?
C - If I showed you what the flag on the boat's mast looked like, could you help me identify it?
D - If I were to describe the boat to you, could you help me identify it?

Go to 93 for your answer.

015

WE KNEW YOU WERE THE ONE FOR THE JOB. COME TO 312
AND WE'LL SHOW YOU WHAT WE'VE FIGURED OUT SO FAR.

016

190
137

017

322

018

WELL I'LL BE, YOU AIN'T HALF BAD! IF YOU'VE COME THIS FAR, THIS ADVENTURE SHOULD BE A PIECE OF CAKE.

FOR SURE! YOU SHOULD APPLY AT NASA OR VAN RYDER GAMES. YOU'VE GOT WHAT IT TAKES.

SALIDOU CONNECTION

MOUSTACHE FOREVER BABY!

AJ ♡ JESSICA

CANADA

CLAP CLAP CLAP

mulot b.

019

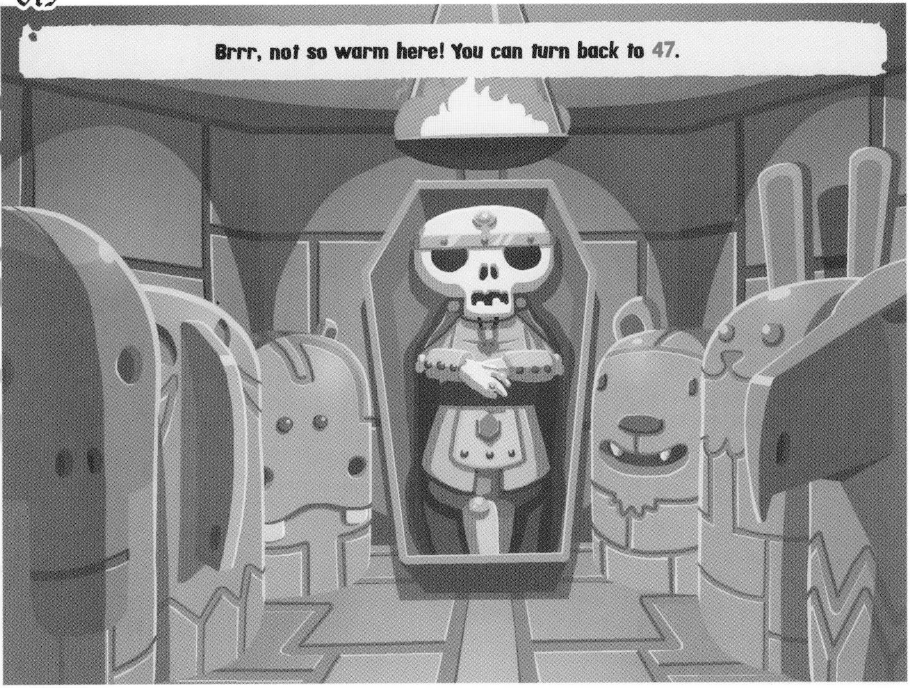

Brrr, not so warm here! You can turn back to 47.

020

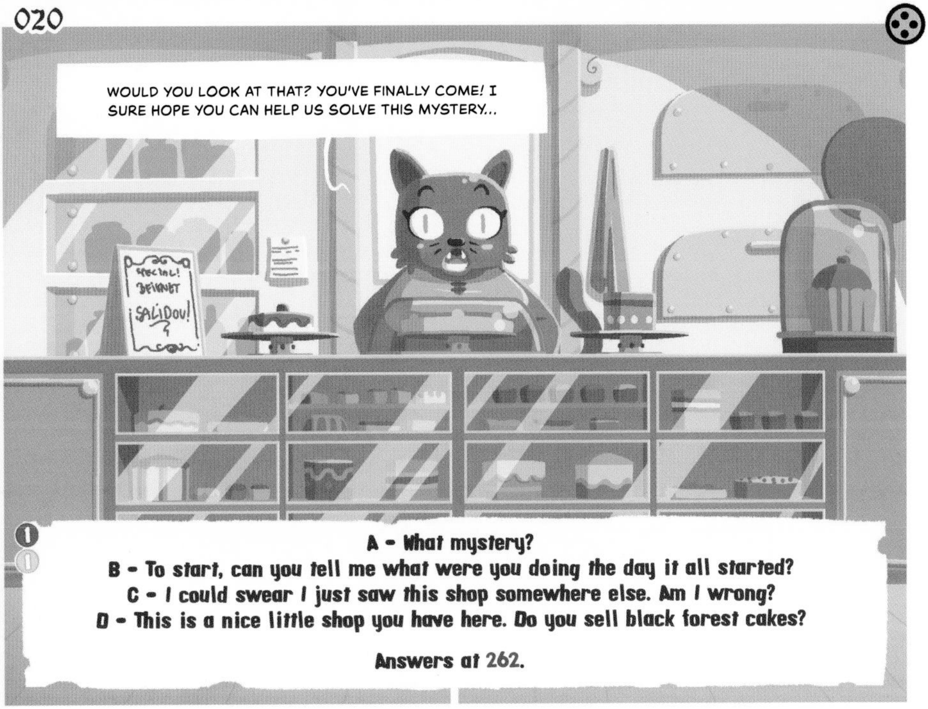

WOULD YOU LOOK AT THAT? YOU'VE FINALLY COME! I SURE HOPE YOU CAN HELP US SOLVE THIS MYSTERY...

A - What mystery?
B - To start, can you tell me what were you doing the day it all started?
C - I could swear I just saw this shop somewhere else. Am I wrong?
D - This is a nice little shop you have here. Do you sell black forest cakes?

Answers at 262.

021

229
281

022

Something really strange is going on here. You can return to 240.

023

143
96

024

HELLO, PIRATE. MY NAME IS RINCEPATEDOUA, THE VILLAGE CHIEF. I KNEW THAT YOU WOULD COME, SOONER OR LATER. YOU'RE WELCOME TO INTERROGATE WHICHEVER VILLAGERS YOU'D LIKE, ESPECIALLY IF IT WILL ALLOW YOU TO HELP US. COME SEE ME AT 53 WHEN YOU'RE FINISHED.

AND IF YOU'D LIKE A LITTLE ISLAND SOUVENIR, GO SEE MARCO.

291
266
122
MARCO

NO, I PROMISE I'M NOT HERE FOR NOTHING, BOSS!
Moose Community
Moose: Centuries of history
Wanesh the Wizard Moose

A - What are these books on the table?
B - In that case, why didn't you transform into an animal?
C - What differentiates you from the other villagers here?
D - If you're innocent, why haven't you left your home?
E - In that case, why did you slam the door in my face the last time?
(You may only ask this question if Tom actually slammed the door in your face.)

Answers at 316.

026

Observe closely, ask the right questions, and most importantly don't cheat, as that would ruin your adventure. Read ONLY the answers to the questions you decide to ask, take time to analyze and reflect on the information you collect. Your adventure starts at 285, pirate! We're counting on you!

027

BLA BLA BLA
BLA BLA
BLA BLA
BLA BLA
BLA

A - I'm looking for some peace and quiet, but something tells me I'm not about to find it here... if you see what I mean.

B - I can sell them to you for 20 gold pieces, but then you have to leave me alone and return to 119 (this choice cancels any other questions asked).

C - Hmm... interesting! Rocks like that aren't found on this island. That red is typical of the mountains on a neighboring island.

D - That it had been right under our noses for a long time.

E - On the nearby small island, populated by the Patikas. They're harmless as long as we remain discreet and don't run in front of them. There is an entrance to a mine at the only spot where you can see the other two islands of the archipelago.

You can now return to 119.

028

Oh dear! While you had your back turned, the path caved in... there must be some way to clear all of this rubble.

029

121

030

Ah yes, one important detail: the Patikas do not tolerate running, plus they're exceptionally good hunters. You die, pierced by a spear, which was poisoned to boot. You can restart on page 2.

031

252

032

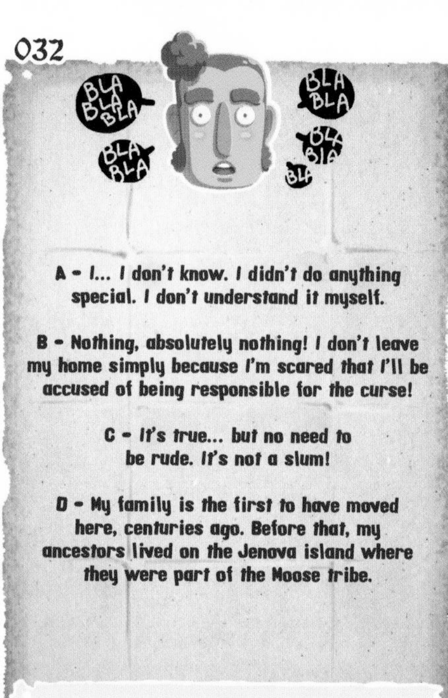

BLA BLA BLA
BLA BLA
BLA BLA
BLA BLA
BLA

A - I... I don't know. I didn't do anything special. I don't understand it myself.

B - Nothing, absolutely nothing! I don't leave my home simply because I'm scared that I'll be accused of being responsible for the curse!

C - It's true... but no need to be rude. It's not a slum!

D - My family is the first to have moved here, centuries ago. Before that, my ancestors lived on the Jenova island where they were part of the Moose tribe.

You can now return to 284.

033

You continue to 194.

034

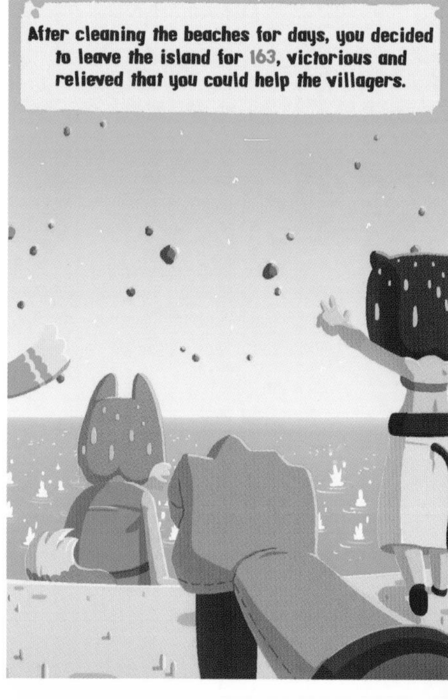

After cleaning the beaches for days, you decided to leave the island for 163, victorious and relieved that you could help the villagers.

035

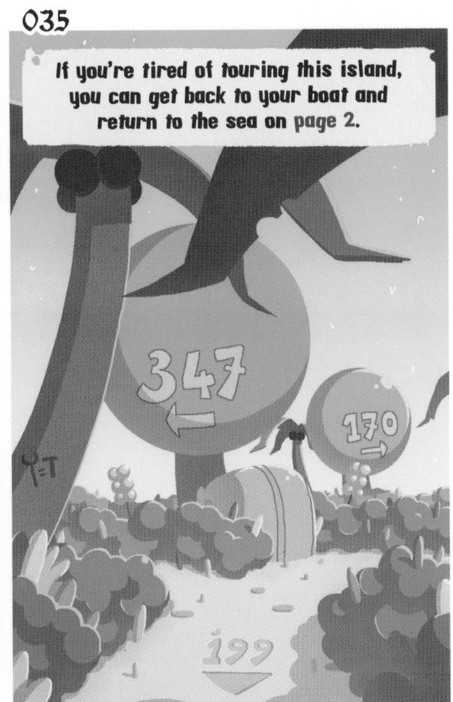
If you're tired of touring this island, you can get back to your boat and return to the sea on page 2.
347
170
199

036

159
304

037

VINCENT, REALLY? GOOD GRIEF! WE MUST GO LOOKING FOR HIM IMMEDIATELY! I ACTUALLY SAW HIM JUST A MOMENT AGO. FOLLOW ME TO 64.

038

I'm pretty sure he didn't understand a word you said. I recommend you salute him, and head to 159.

039

No use hanging around here... Hurry to 284.

040

Thanks to you, the curse seems to have stopped! You can get back on your ship at 124.

041

The sea is calm. You find its tranquility relaxing. Breathe it in and continue to 113.

042

BLA BLA BLA

BLA BLA

BLA BLA
BLA

BLA BLA

A - You don't find her strange? Always hiding, fleeing... You should really look into her, I'm telling you.

B - A lovely woman that the curse transformed into a cheetah. She lives in the middle of the village.

C - An extraordinary cook. She lives by the sea.

D - Me? Heavens, no!

E - I... hmm... a little further, in the forest. It's the house with the straw roof.

You can retrace your steps to 143 or continue along to 51.

043

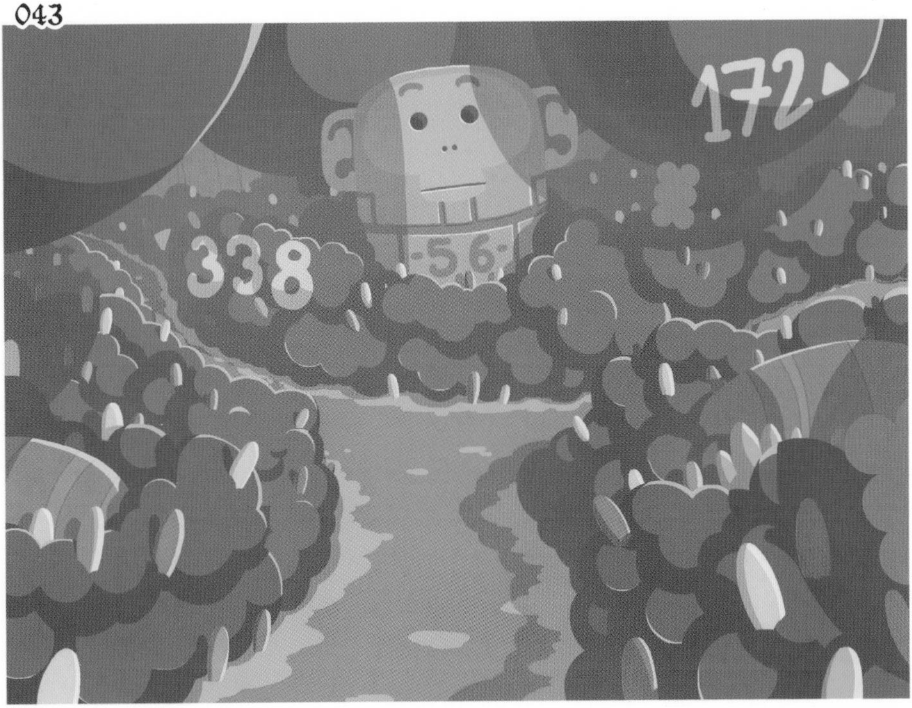

172
338
56

044

sharks for dummies
Simon Foirfouille

After having a look around this little house, return to 177.

045

If you have more than 12 Agility, you can return to 240. Otherwise, go to 167.

046

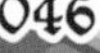

COULD YOU PLEASE LEAVE MICHEL 542 ALONE?

A - YES, I'M THE OWNER OF THIS SHOP.

B - WHAT ARE YOU TALKING ABOUT, WEIRDO?

C - I THINK THE PERSON WHO RETURNED MICHEL 374 HAD SOMETHING TO DO WITH IT.

D - YES... THE KNIGHT... HE DIDN'T EXACTLY INSPIRE CONFIDENCE IN ME. I SHOULD HAVE TRUSTED MY INSTINCTS.

E - NO PROBLEM, THAT'LL BE 20 GOLD COINS. YOU WANT IT?

You can leave to 24.

047

71

048

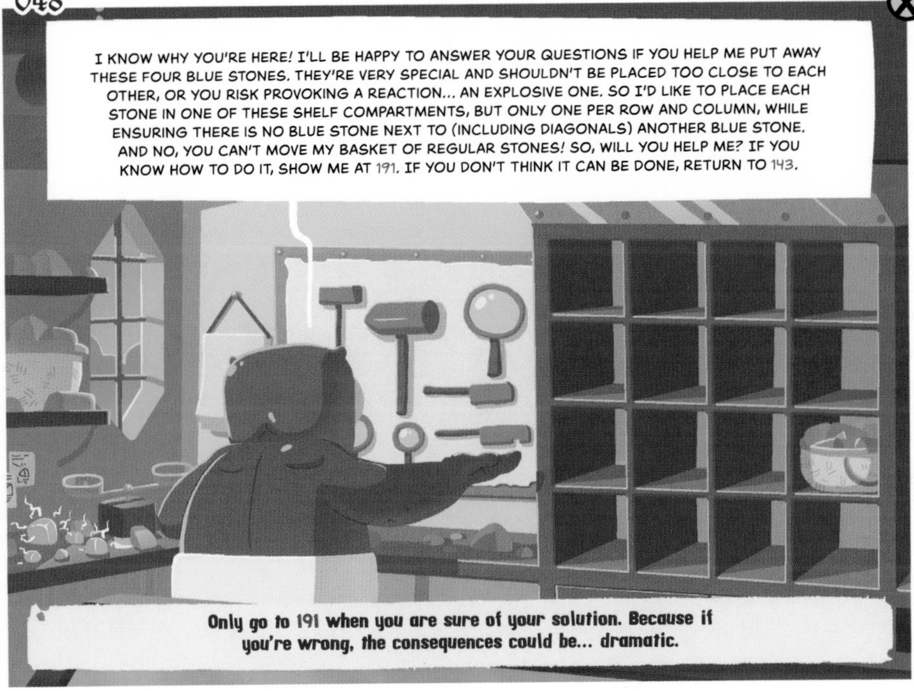

I KNOW WHY YOU'RE HERE! I'LL BE HAPPY TO ANSWER YOUR QUESTIONS IF YOU HELP ME PUT AWAY THESE FOUR BLUE STONES. THEY'RE VERY SPECIAL AND SHOULDN'T BE PLACED TOO CLOSE TO EACH OTHER, OR YOU RISK PROVOKING A REACTION... AN EXPLOSIVE ONE. SO I'D LIKE TO PLACE EACH STONE IN ONE OF THESE SHELF COMPARTMENTS, BUT ONLY ONE PER ROW AND COLUMN, WHILE ENSURING THERE IS NO BLUE STONE NEXT TO (INCLUDING DIAGONALS) ANOTHER BLUE STONE. AND NO, YOU CAN'T MOVE MY BASKET OF REGULAR STONES! SO, WILL YOU HELP ME? IF YOU KNOW HOW TO DO IT, SHOW ME AT 191. IF YOU DON'T THINK IT CAN BE DONE, RETURN TO 143.

Only go to 191 when you are sure of your solution. Because if you're wrong, the consequences could be... dramatic.

049

If you have more than 15 intuition, go to 59 before heading to 168.

050

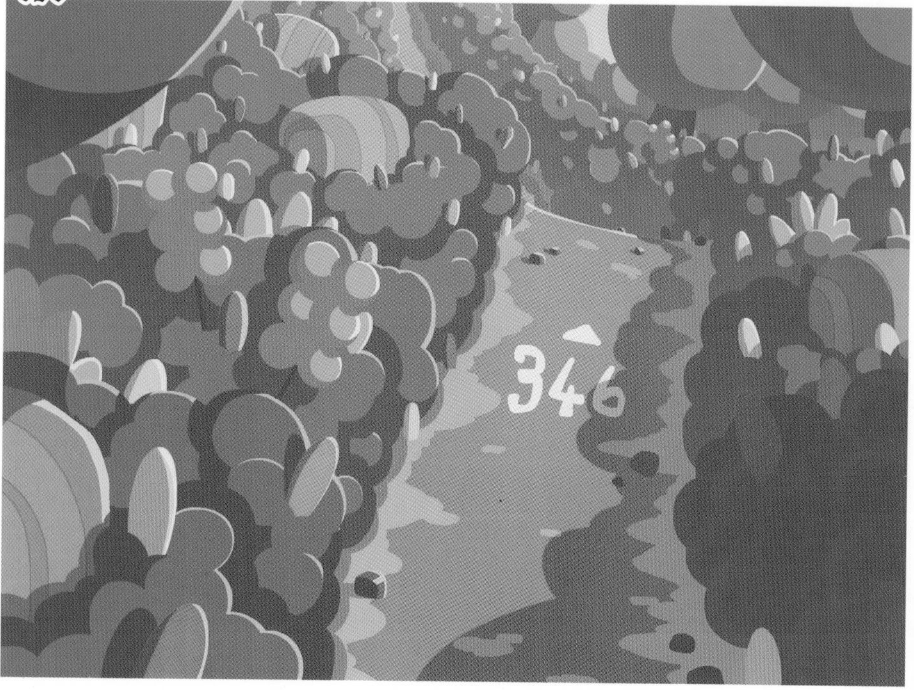

346

051

197

052

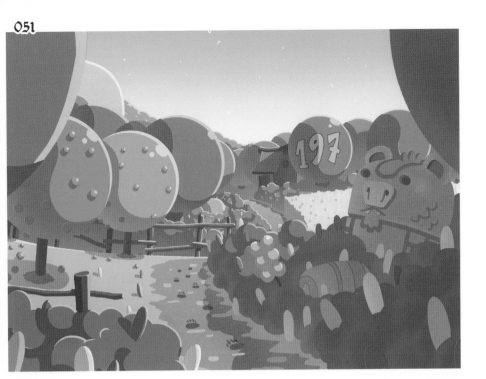

FOR YOUR SAKE, I HOPE THAT YOU HAVE INDEED SOLVE THE MYSTERY OF THE CURSE, AS A NEW PAIR OF INVESTIGATORS HAVE JUST ARRIVED. IF YOU'RE WRONG, THEY'LL BE TAKING OVER FROM HERE. SO, WHAT WILL YOU DO TO RESTORE OUR APPEARANCE?

A: DESTROY THE TOTEMS
B: DESTROY THE BURIED CITY.
C: EAT MORE WATERMELONS.
D: RECOVER THE SACRED RUBY.
E: PLUG THE ISLAND'S VOLCANO.
F: IMPRISON LÉONA.
G: THERE'S NOTHING WE CAN DO.
H: IT'S ALL THE MOON'S FAULT.
I: WE MUST DEFEAT THE SKELETON GUARDIANS.
J: WE MUST KILL THE PATIKAS.
K: WE MUST CAPTURE THE INHABITANTS OF SHUKANET.
L: IT'S ALL YOUR FAULT.
M: DESTROY THE NEXT BOAT THAT SHOWS UP.
N: RECOVER THE TREASURES STOLEN BY A KNIGHT.

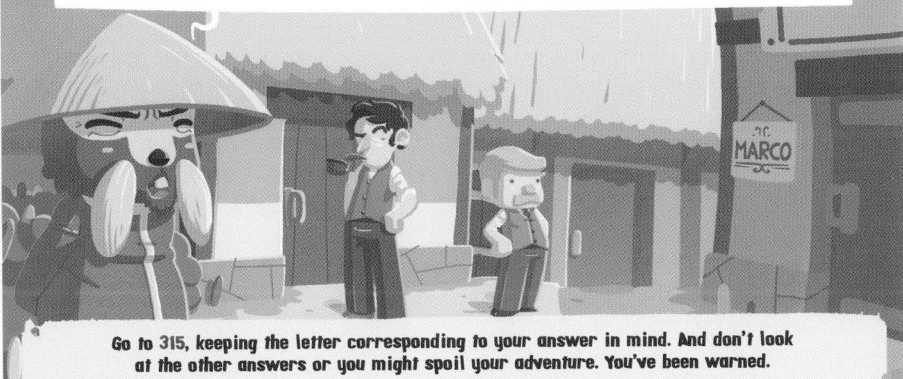
MARCO
Go to 315, keeping the letter corresponding to your answer in mind. And don't look at the other answers or you might spoil your adventure. You've been warned.

053

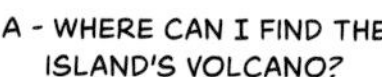

A - WHERE CAN I FIND THE ISLAND'S VOLCANO?

B - WHO CAN HELP ME SHED SOME LIGHT ON THE MYSTERY OF THIS CURSE?

C - I HEARD THAT A BOAT WAS SEEN NEAR YOUR ISLAND, SHORTLY BEFORE THE CURSE FELL. WHAT DO YOU KNOW ABOUT IT?

D - THE STRANGE TOTEMS THAT CAN BE SEEN ON SHUKANET ISLAND SEEM LIKE THEY MIGHT BE LINKED TO ALL OF THIS. DO YOU HAVE ANY ON THIS ISLAND?

E - DO YOU HAVE ANY ADVICE TO OFFER?

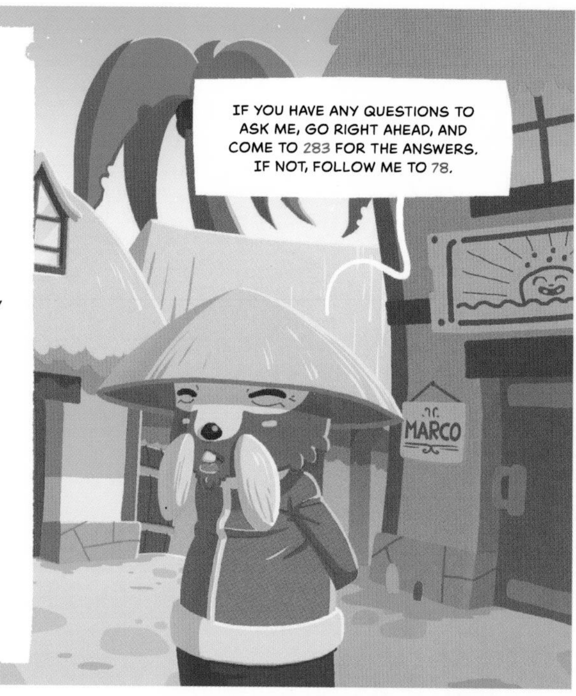
IF YOU HAVE ANY QUESTIONS TO ASK ME, GO RIGHT AHEAD, AND COME TO 283 FOR THE ANSWERS. IF NOT, FOLLOW ME TO 78.
MARCO

054

055

PIRATE, YOU ARE A MEDIOCRE INVESTIGATOR AND YOU HAVE WRONGLY ACCUSED POOR TOM! DESPITE THAT, I BELIEVE YOU COULD STILL PROVE USEFUL. YOU SHOULD RETURN TO THE VILLAGE ENTRANCE AND CONTINUE YOUR INVESTIGATION.

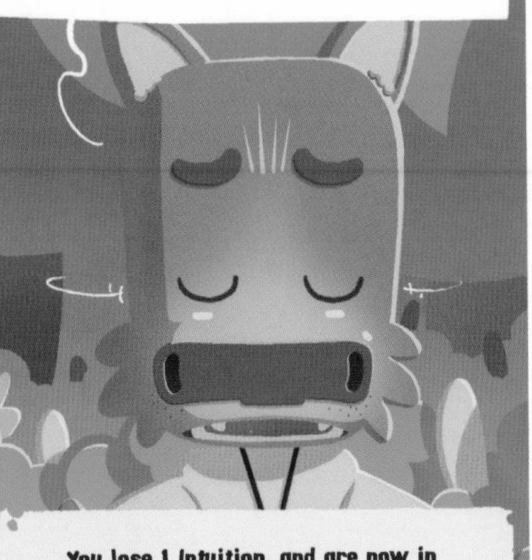

You lose 1 *Intuition*, and are now in possession of an orange card. Head to 285.

056

If you have a magnifying glass, you can look closer at 80. If not, return to 43.

057

GOOD GRIEF, BUT OF COURSE! THE TOTEMS... THE TOTEMS ARE WHAT'S CAUSING THE CURSE. WHAT SHOULD WE DO, NOBLE PIRATE?

If you think that you must arm yourselves with hammers and chisels to destroy the totems, go to 200. If you believe the inhabitants must leave the island, go to 40. Before making your decision, would you like to see if there are similar totems on neighboring islands? Go to 135. You just don't know what to do? Go to 140.

058

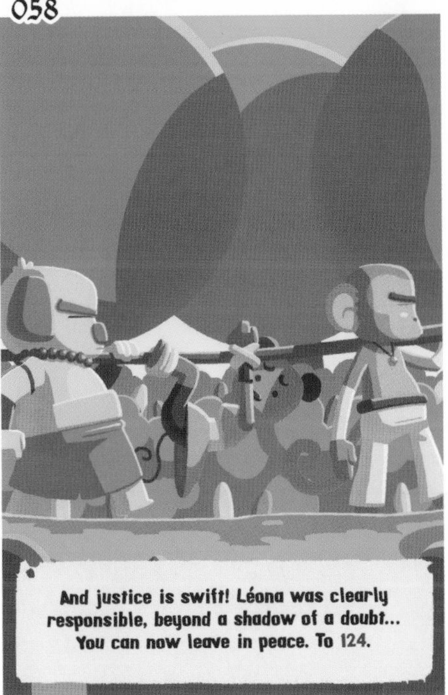

And justice is swift! Léona was clearly responsible, beyond a shadow of a doubt... You can now leave in peace. To 124.

059

060

061

When the sailor told you to avoid the currents, they meant it! You're definitely going to die, but you get to choose how. Were you: sucked into a whirlpool, eaten by a shark, or choked by the tentacles of a giant octopus? Whichever you choose, you can restart your adventure on page 2.

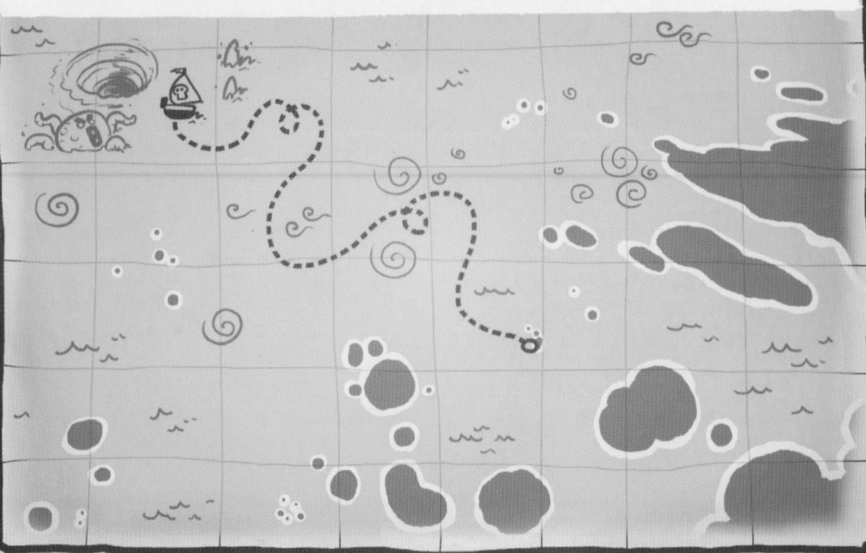

062

From now on, you're welcome to interrogate the people you meet. This symbol ❷ indicates the number of questions you're allowed to ask. The yellow symbol is for players aged 14 or younger. Once you've chosen your questions, go to 351 to read the answers. Careful, now! Make sure to only look at the answers corresponding to your question, otherwise you risk spoiling your adventure!

LIFE SURE IS IRONIC, EH?

❷
❸

A - How were you transformed?
B - How do you like being a shark?
C - Do you swim better now?
D - How much do those fish cost?
E - Where do you live?

063

A-ha, you've read Pirates: The Great Chase, haven't you? You learned to watch out for cracks in the road, and therefore avoided a landslide that probably would've caused a few problems for you. Add 1 to your Intuition.

95

064

3314

065

Ah yes, well *that*... is quite impressive... You succeed in breaking his barrier if you have more than 15 *Intelligence*, and go to 331. You can also try to throwing a rock at him at 139, or just leave to 43.

066

293

067

DON'T HURT ME... I DIDN'T DO ANYTHING, I SWEAR.

2
3

A - Why didn't you turn into an animal?
B - What are you hiding?
C - It's funny. Your house looks way uglier from the outside.
D - How long have you lived on this island?

Answers at 32.

068

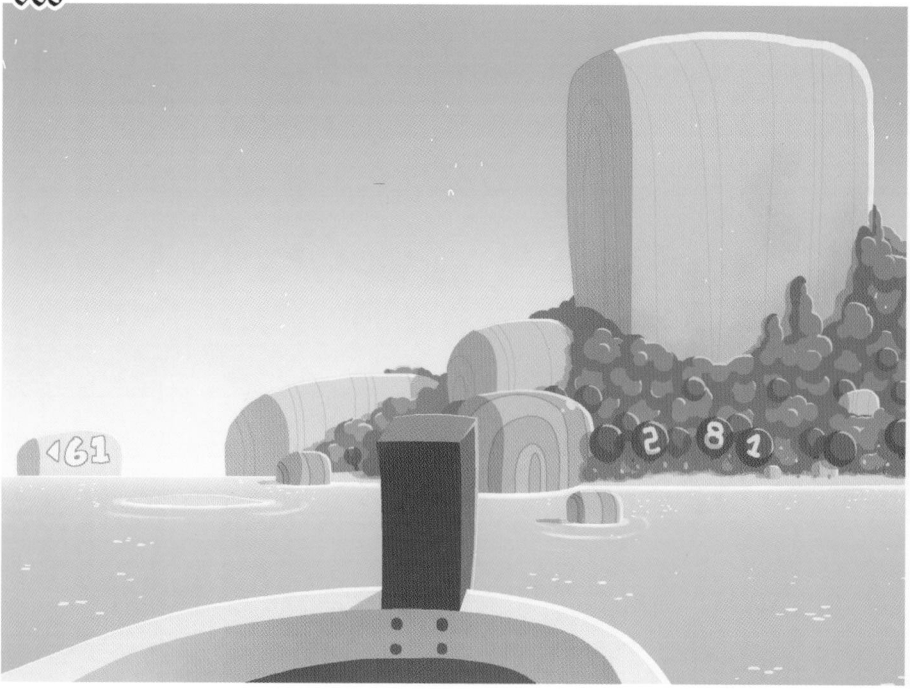

◁61
2
8
1

069

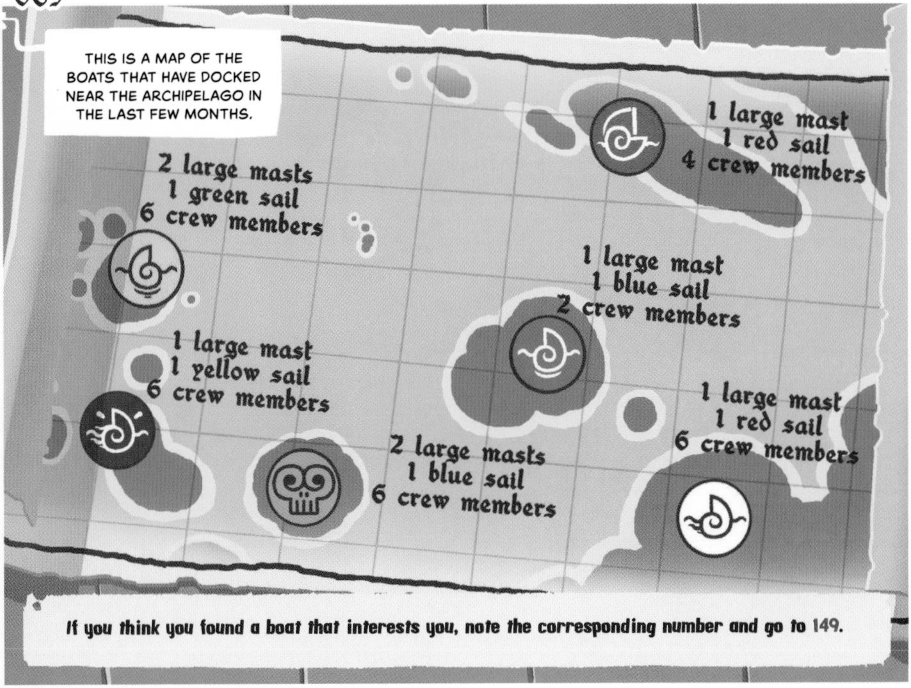

THIS IS A MAP OF THE BOATS THAT HAVE DOCKED NEAR THE ARCHIPELAGO IN THE LAST FEW MONTHS.

1 large mast
1 red sail
4 crew members

2 large masts
1 green sail
6 crew members

1 large mast
1 blue sail
2 crew members

1 large mast
1 yellow sail
6 crew members

1 large mast
1 red sail
6 crew members

2 large masts
1 blue sail
6 crew members

If you think you found a boat that interests you, note the corresponding number and go to 149.

070

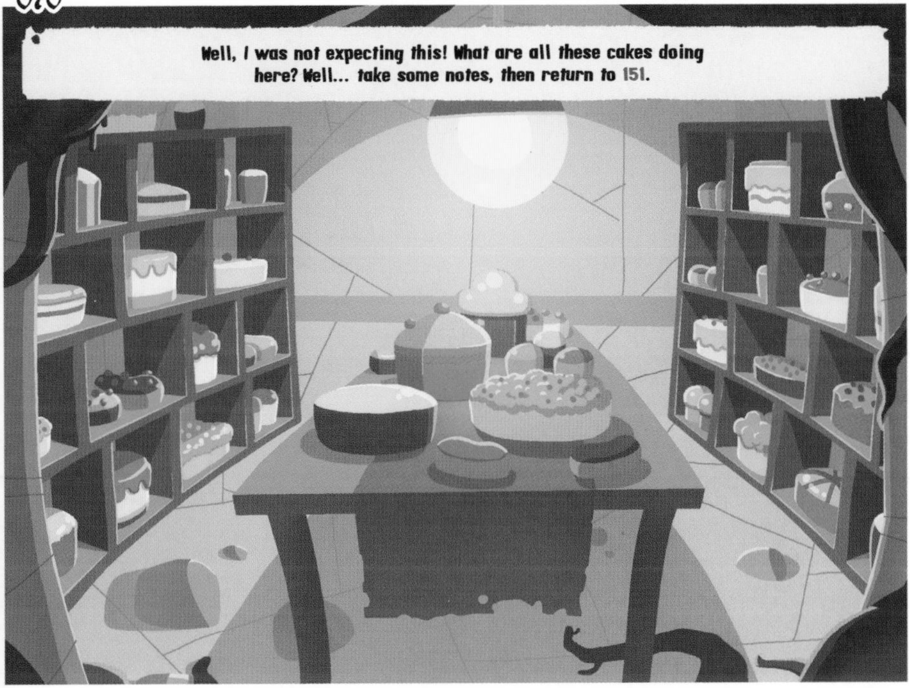

Well, I was not expecting this! What are all these cakes doing here? Well... take some notes, then return to 151.

071

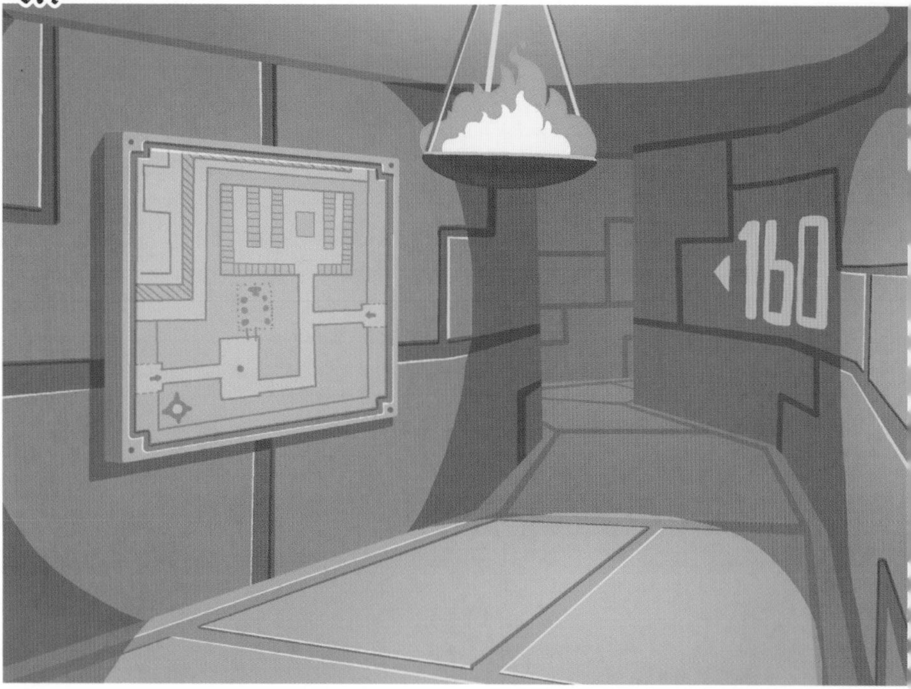

072

073

Sooo... the sea's pretty big... go to 209.

074

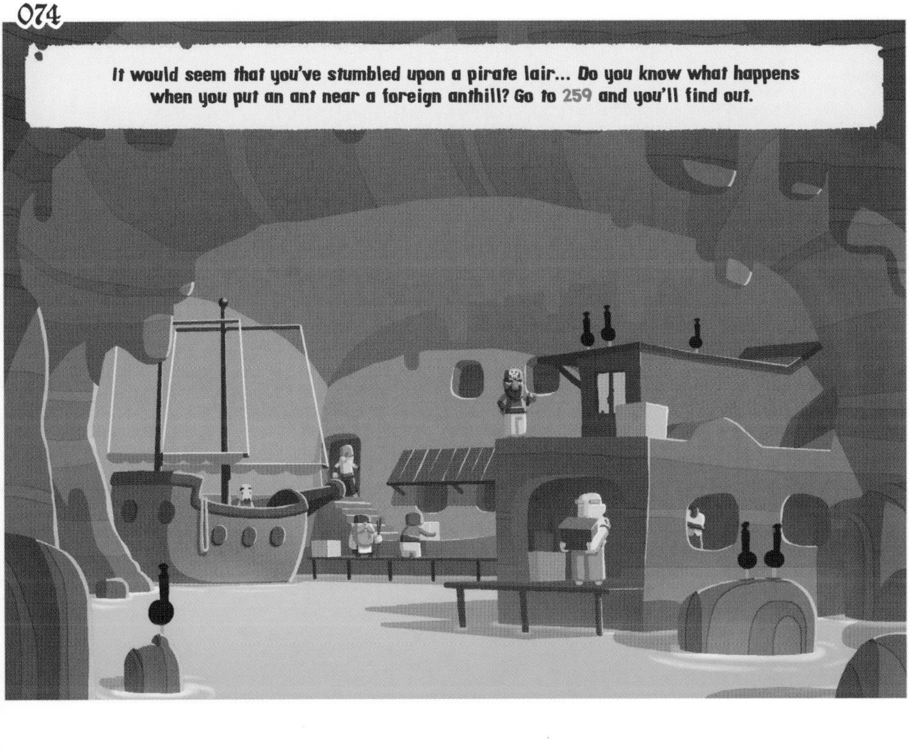

It would seem that you've stumbled upon a pirate lair... Do you know what happens when you put an ant near a foreign anthill? Go to 259 and you'll find out.

075

214

076

HELLO THERE. LET ME GUESS, YOU'RE THE INVESTIGATOR WHO'S SUPPOSED TO GET US OUT OF THIS? I WOULD LIKE TO ANSWER YOUR QUESTIONS, BUT YOU'LL HAVE TO ANSWER MINE FIRST: LOOKING AROUND THIS PANEL, DO YOU SEE MY FRIEND, GRIBLI? GIVE ME YOUR ANSWER AT 186.

077

OH REALLY? NO SUSPECTS? IF YOU'D LIKE TO INTERROGATE THE VILLAGERS AGAIN, RETURN TO 285. BUT THIS TIME, YOU CAN ONLY ASK 1 QUESTION OF EACH OF THEM. ON THE OTHER HAND, IF YOU HAVE ANOTHER IDEA OF WHAT CAUSED THE CURSE, COME SEE ME AT 125.

If you have no doubts about another person, you are certainly mistaken. Ah! Naturally, as you pass through the village again, you cannot benefit from any bonuses you had already acquired.

078

I INVITE YOU TO ENTER THE JENOVA FOREST, PROUD ADVENTURER. YOU'LL DEFINITELY FIND THE MISSING CLUES YOU NEED TO SOLVE THE MYSTERY OF THE CURSE. ONCE YOU THINK YOU'VE COLLECTED ENOUGH CLUES TO REVERSE THE CURSE, OR YOU BELIEVE YOU'RE JUST GOING IN CIRCLES, COME TO 52.

276

079

A - Every... everything is your fault? How in the devil did that come to be?

B - If that's the case, would you allow me to tie your hands and take you to your leader?

C - You're the one responsible for the curse?

D - Jasmine is in the know too, isn't she?

Answers at 226.

080

Thanks to your magnifying glass, you spotted a small hole. You decide to shove a twig in it, which triggers a mechanism that opens a hiding place. You find a magnificent broach. You can return to 43.

081

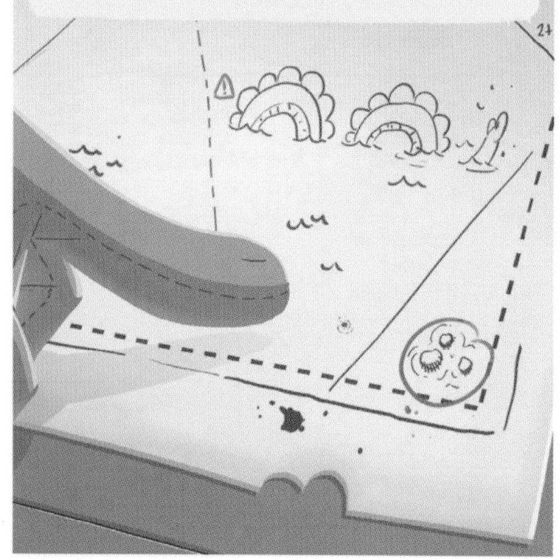
If you finished "Pirates: The City of Skulls" and were named second in command, you're able to convince them to point you to this place, at 199, before heading to the archipelago. If not, the captain doesn't really appreciated your attitude and docks you 10 gold pieces. Return to page 2.

082

Great... in the end, having this torch didn't really do anything, since the path is blocked. You can return to 85. And quit your grumbling, it's not that far. It's on the next page. And, of course, you may no longer go to 302.

083

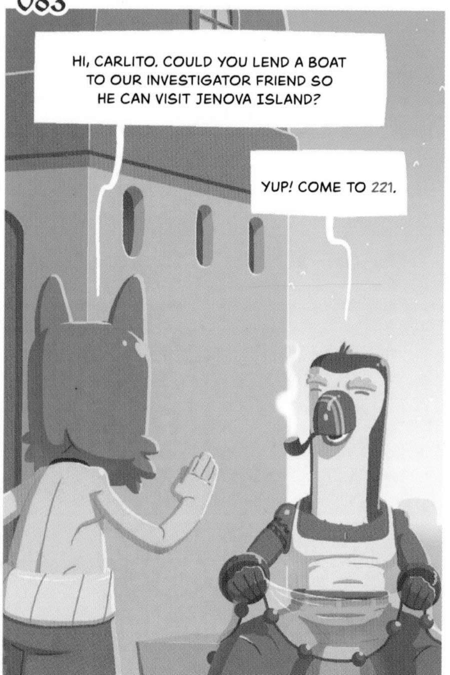
HI, CARLITO. COULD YOU LEND A BOAT TO OUR INVESTIGATOR FRIEND SO HE CAN VISIT JENOVA ISLAND?
YUP! COME TO 221.

084

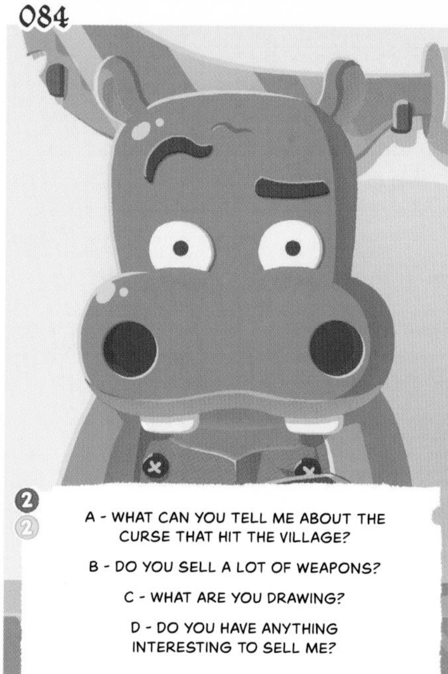
2
2
A - WHAT CAN YOU TELL ME ABOUT THE CURSE THAT HIT THE VILLAGE?
B - DO YOU SELL A LOT OF WEAPONS?
C - WHAT ARE YOU DRAWING?
D - DO YOU HAVE ANYTHING INTERESTING TO SELL ME?
ANSWERS AT 324.

085

95
236

086

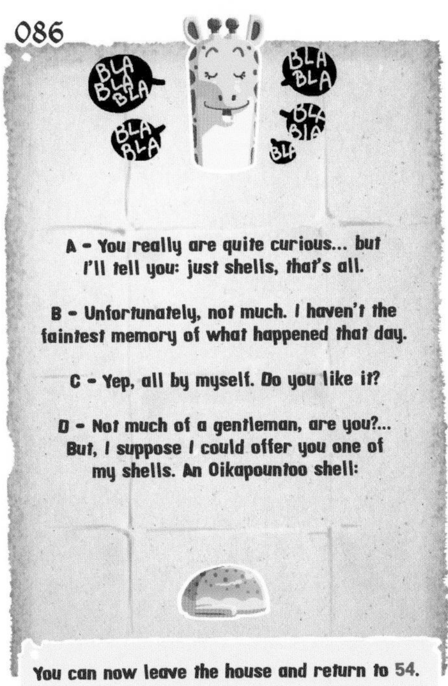
BLA BLA BLA
BLA BLA
BLA BLA

A - You really are quite curious... but I'll tell you: just shells, that's all.

B - Unfortunately, not much. I haven't the faintest memory of what happened that day.

C - Yep, all by myself. Do you like it?

D - Not much of a gentleman, are you?... But, I suppose I could offer you one of my shells. An Oikapountoo shell:

You can now leave the house and return to 54.

087

The bridge snaps underneath your feet, but you manage to grab hold of a branch at the last moment. During your fall, your bag opens and three objects fall out. If you have at least 8 Agility, you're able to grab hold of one as it falls, and only lose two objects instead. Choose the objects you lost and remove them from your bag. Then go to 320.

KRAK!

I HAD NO IDEA THIS RUBY WAS SO POWERFUL. HAD I KNOWN, I NEVER WOULD HAVE TAKEN IT, I PROMISE YOU THAT.

ON THE OTHER HAND, I CAN'T EXACTLY GIVE IT TO YOU WITHOUT RECEIVING ANYTHING IN RETURN. I'LL LET IT GO FOR 500 GOLD PIECES.
You can sell your objects at 311. Come back when you're done.

IT'S ALL YOURS, BRAVE ADVENTURER! WOULD YOU LIKE A GIFT BOX?

Bravo, pirate! I believe that, this time, you've finally accomplished your mission. Set sail for Jenova!

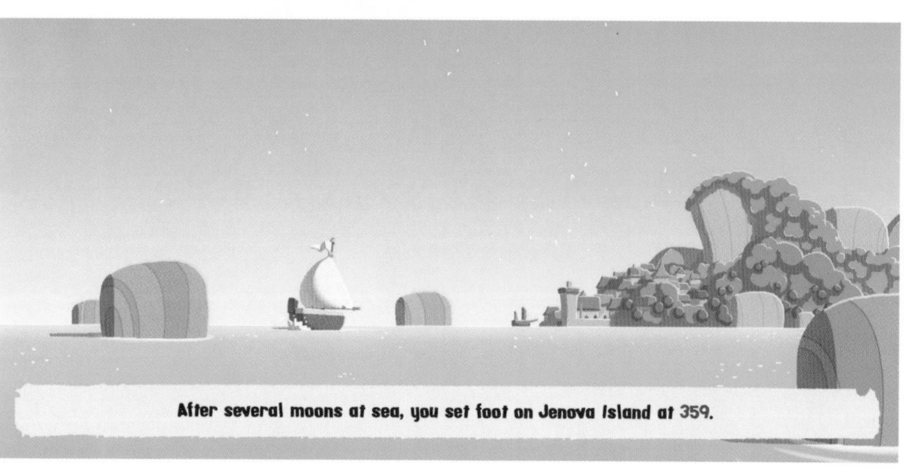
After several moons at sea, you set foot on Jenova Island at 359.

089

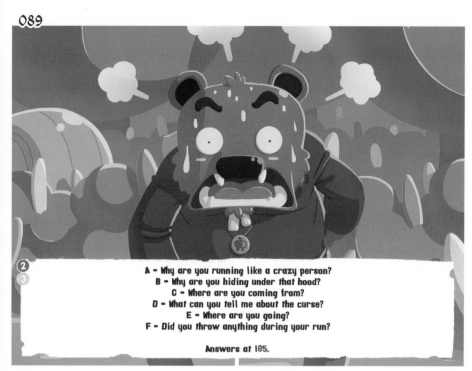

A - Why are you running like a crazy person?
B - Why are you hiding under that hood?
C - Where are you coming from?
D - What can you tell me about the curse?
E - Where are you going?
F - Did you throw anything during your run?

Answers at 185.

090

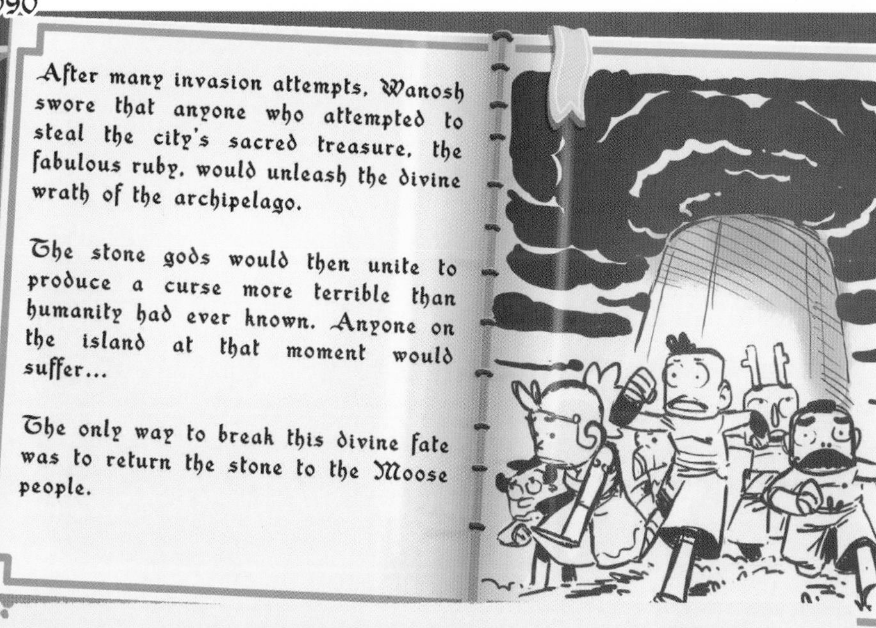

After many invasion attempts, Wanosh swore that anyone who attempted to steal the city's sacred treasure, the fabulous ruby, would unleash the divine wrath of the archipelago.

The stone gods would then unite to produce a curse more terrible than humanity had ever known. Anyone on the island at that moment would suffer...

The only way to break this divine fate was to return the stone to the Moose people.

Whoa, hey now... This is pretty interesting, no? You can return to 160 or head right back to 16.

091

220

092

288

093

BLA BLA BLA
BLA BLA
BLA BLA
BLA BLA
BLA

A - Not really, no. If you had a description, I could help you, but... We could possibly look at the manifests of the merchant ships. Come to 69.

B - Absolutely not. I was at sea at the time. Not that far... but not that close either.

C - Certainly, follow me to 69. We can look more closely using the manifests of the merchant ships.

D - Yes, I should be able to help you. Come to 69, where it's a little quieter.

If the answer doesn't suit you, but you still believe a boat is how this all started, go to 287. However, if you think that you may have been wrong, go to 125, and lose 1 Intuition.

094

I DON'T REALLY KNOW WHAT HE'S UP TO, BUT HE OFTEN GOES OUT IN THE MIDDLE OF THE NIGHT. HE'S CAUTIOUS, ALWAYS LOOKING AROUND TO MAKE SURE NO ONE IS FOLLOWING HIM, AND OFTEN COMES BACK WITH HIS HANDS FULL... OF WHAT, I DON'T KNOW. HE ALSO WEARS A STRANGE PENDANT IN THE SHAPE OF A CRANE EMBEDDED WITH A CRESCENT MOON.

You can return to 240.

095

302
85

096

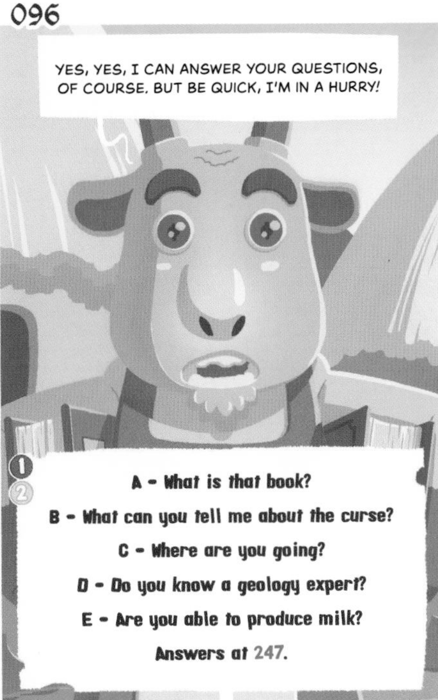
YES, YES, I CAN ANSWER YOUR QUESTIONS, OF COURSE. BUT BE QUICK, I'M IN A HURRY!
A - What is that book?
B - What can you tell me about the curse?
C - Where are you going?
D - Do you know a geology expert?
E - Are you able to produce milk?
Answers at 247.

097

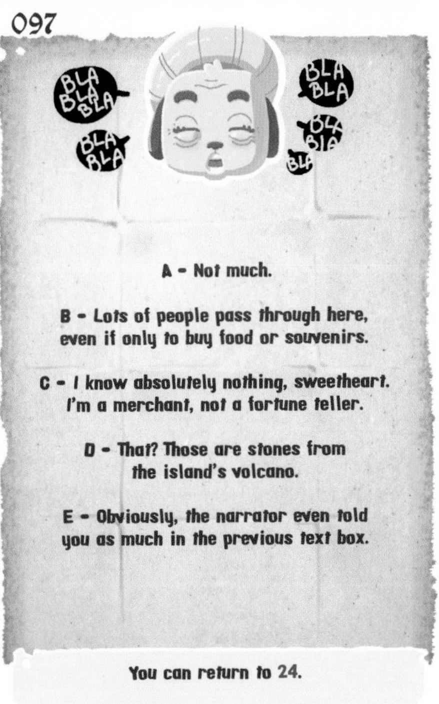
BLA BLA BLA
BLA BLA
BLA BLA
A - Not much.
B - Lots of people pass through here, even if only to buy food or souvenirs.
C - I know absolutely nothing, sweetheart. I'm a merchant, not a fortune teller.
D - That? Those are stones from the island's volcano.
E - Obviously, the narrator even told you as much in the previous text box.
You can return to 24.

098

A - Your mom told me that you enjoy contemplating the horizon from the bridge near her house?
B - What are you drawing?
C - Is your mom making an apple pie?
D - How's business?
Answers at 205.

099

LISTEN WELL, PIRATE, WHICH ANIMAL IS ABLE TO JUMP HIGHER THAN THE TALLEST OF TREES?
ONCE YOU HAVE YOUR ANSWER, GO TO 104.

100

Magnificent discovery... but I must insist, don't go rooting through every bush in the forests, or we're going to be in here for ten days! Return to 288.

101

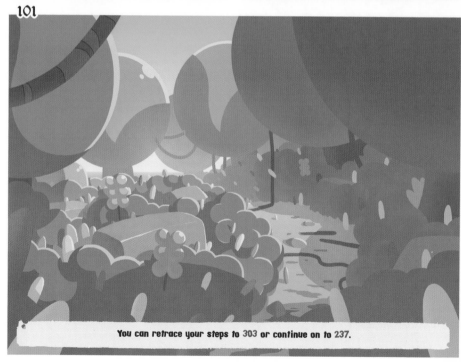

You can retrace your steps to 303 or continue on to 237.

102
START

103

A - Do you need help?

B - What can you tell me about the curse?

C - What are you carrying in your basket?

D - Where are you coming from?

Answers at 189.

104

By composing the name of the animal you wish to visit, you'll obtain the panel number where they can be found. If you're done here, go to 78.

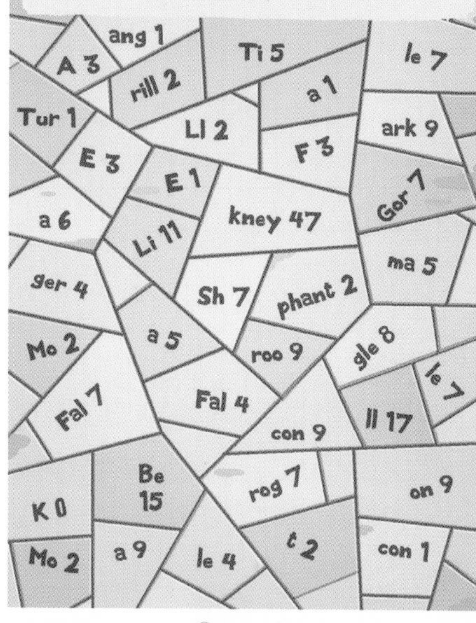

A 3
ang 1
rill 2
Ti 5
le 7
a 1
Tur 1
Li 2
ark 9
E 3
F 3
E 1
kney 47
Gor 7
a 6
Li 11
ma 5
ger 4
Sh 7
phant 2
a 5
Mo 2
roo 9
gle 8
le 7
Fal 7
Fal 4
ll 17
con 9
Be 15
rog 7
on 9
K 0
Mo 2
a 9
le 4
t 2
con 1

105

Your landing was a little rough. The crash gave you a concussion. Lose 1 Intelligence point. Now, to find a way out of here. Ooh, I know... look for a number to follow.

106

A - Oh, leave me be then. I don't have time for such foolishness! (You must return to 143 and cannot ask any further questions.)

B - Right now.

C - Spiced breads. All kinds of cookies.

D - By the window behind me. (Once you've read the answers to your questions, you can take a look at the window at 243.)

E - Like what, for example? The fact that I transformed into an animal? Why is that so bad, anyway?

F - Heavens no, inspector! This is the seventh time now in three months. And I'm not alone. Henrietta, who lives just outside the village, deals with theft regularly.

You can return to 143.

107

108

Fortunately, you can't continue on. You can turn around and return to 151.

109

HMM, YES... WHAT? INDEED, I AM ELLIOT... HOW? YOU'D LIKE TO BUY ME THINGS? YOU SHOULD HAVE TOLD ME EARLIER! COME TO 330, MY FRIEND!

110

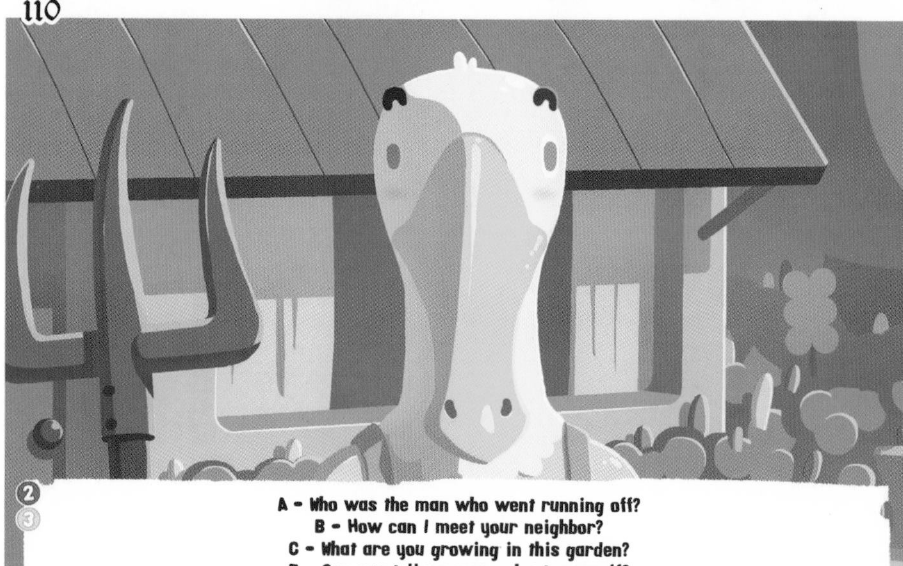

A - Who was the man who went running off?
B - How can I meet your neighbor?
C - What are you growing in this garden?
D - Can you tell me more about yourself?
E - What can you tell me about your neighbor?
F - Do you think a resident of the village is responsible for the curse?

Answers at 157.

If you feel like it, you can ask him a question.

A - Coco want a cracker?

B - Say: "Coco is beautiful."

C - Does Coco love cocoa and Van Ryder books?

Go to 340 for your answer. If you'd rather not ask him a question, return to 171.

61
68

It looks like you've arrived. You can dock at 245 and interrogate the captain of that ship.

245

114

A - It appears that you have an interesting theory concerning the curse, or so Maurice told me. Go to 129.

B - It appears that you have an interesting theory concerning the curse, or so Philipo told me. Go to 269.

C - It appears that you have an interesting theory concerning the curse, or so Jasmine told me. Go to 174.

D - It appears that you have an interesting theory concerning the curse, or so Netanel told me. Go to 282.

Warning: if you had bad information or chose the wrong question, you will have to return to 240 and you can no longer interrogate Gauthier.

115

BLA BLA BLA

BLA BLA

A - Of course. Come to 286 so I can show it to you. (If you asked two questions, this answer prevents you from reading the second one.)

B - Absolutely not. I haven't observed anything strange, and I don't know how you could've come to such a conclusion.

C - Actually... Some time ago, a little before the curse hit us, a ship dropped anchor near Jenova Island. A merchant ship, I figure, because it's coat of arms had a blue background.

D - Naturally, I think you would learn more by exploring Jenova Island. It's all coming from over there, if you ask me.

E - At least twenty good years, my friend.

F - Oh, that? It's nothing, just some grilled eggplant with a drizzle of olive oil.

If you still think the moon is linked to the curse, go to 140. If you have a new theory, return to 125, and subtract 1 Intuition point.

116

If you see these symbols on a wall, apply this explosive gel to blow it up. You can return to 277.

explosive gel
19432
8:★

117

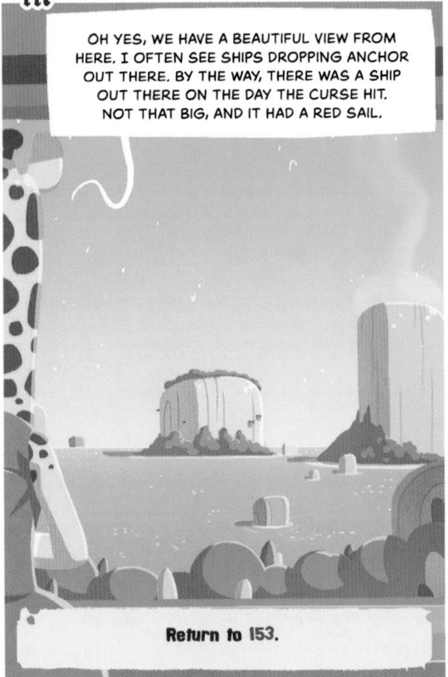
OH YES, WE HAVE A BEAUTIFUL VIEW FROM HERE. I OFTEN SEE SHIPS DROPPING ANCHOR OUT THERE. BY THE WAY, THERE WAS A SHIP OUT THERE ON THE DAY THE CURSE HIT. NOT THAT BIG, AND IT HAD A RED SAIL.

Return to 153.

118

DAMN!

Bad luck. It turns out that the next ship to approach Jenova was the one belonging to your captain, who was coming to pick you up. Your adventure ends here. You can restart at page 2.

119

If you don't know how to enter these houses, turn back to 195.

Mrs. ix

Mr Neetneves

120

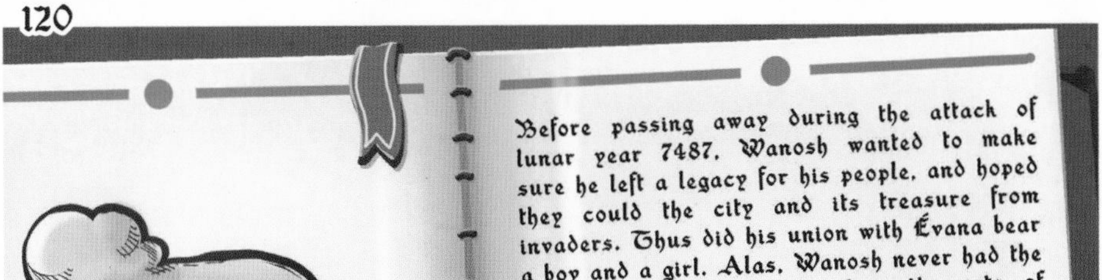

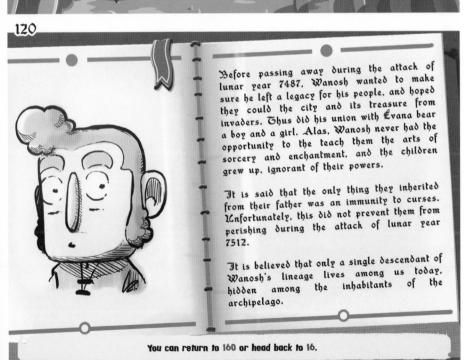

Before passing away during the attack of lunar year 7487, Wanosh wanted to make sure he left a legacy for his people, and hoped they could the city and its treasure from invaders. Thus did his union with Évana bear a boy and a girl. Alas, Wanosh never had the opportunity to the teach them the arts of sorcery and enchantment, and the children grew up, ignorant of their powers.

It is said that the only thing they inherited from their father was an immunity to curses. Unfortunately, this did not prevent them from perishing during the attack of lunar year 7512.

It is believed that only a single descendant of Wanosh's lineage lives among us today, hidden among the inhabitants of the archipelago.

You can return to 160 or head back to 16.

121

2
3

A - What are you doing here?
B - Are you selling these stones?
C - I found these volcanic stones. Can you tell me anything about them? (You may only ask this question if you have these rocks in your possession.)
D - What can you tell me about the terrible curse that rocked this village?
E - Can you tell me where I can find beautiful, precious stones?

Answers at 27.

122

1
1

A - Are you the store owner?
B - How are you able to talk while inside a fishbowl?
C - What can you tell me about the curse?
D - Did you see anyone suspicious shortly before the curse hit?
E - Would it bother you if I took a harpoon?

Answers at 46.

123

WHERE ARE YOU, MY LITTLE TIG... UHH... I... YES? THIS IS FOR...?

Yikes! You've definitely uncovered some sort of secret, but... I'm not certain it's the one you're investigating. The village chief is furious and wishes to speak with you at 175.

124

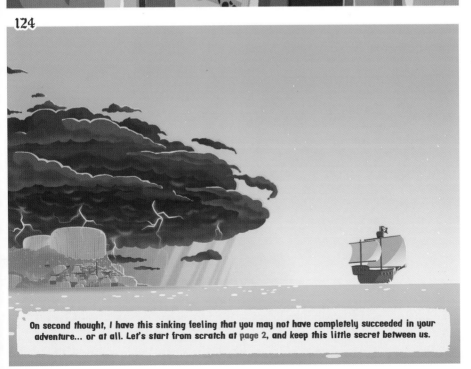

On second thought, I have this sinking feeling that you may not have completely succeeded in your adventure... or at all. Let's start from scratch at page 2, and keep this little secret between us.

- If you think that the curse is just some sort of coincidence and there's nothing to be done about it, go to 163.
- If you think the curse is linked to the strange sculptures hidden in the jungle, go to 57.
- If you think it has something to do with the red volcanic stones, go to 307.
- If you think it all started on Jenova Island, go to 135.
- If you think the moon is connected somehow, go to 249.
- If you think that you need to investigate a ship, go to 297.
- If your theory isn't listed here, perhaps you should return to the village at 285.

Important: you can only ask one question of each person.

126

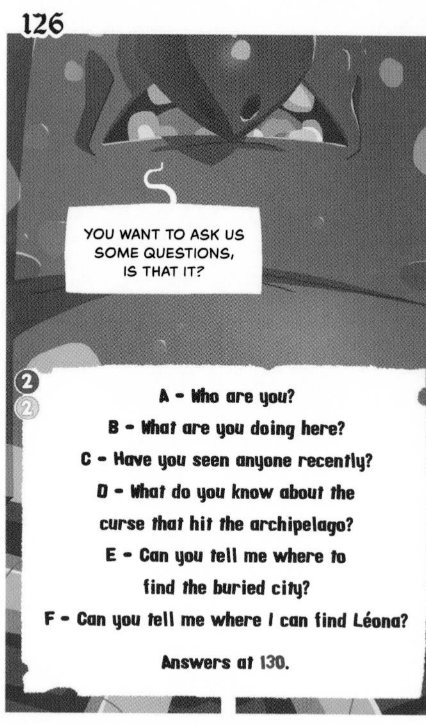
YOU WANT TO ASK US SOME QUESTIONS, IS THAT IT?

A - Who are you?

B - What are you doing here?

C - Have you seen anyone recently?

D - What do you know about the curse that hit the archipelago?

E - Can you tell me where to find the buried city?

F - Can you tell me where I can find Léona?

Answers at 130.

127

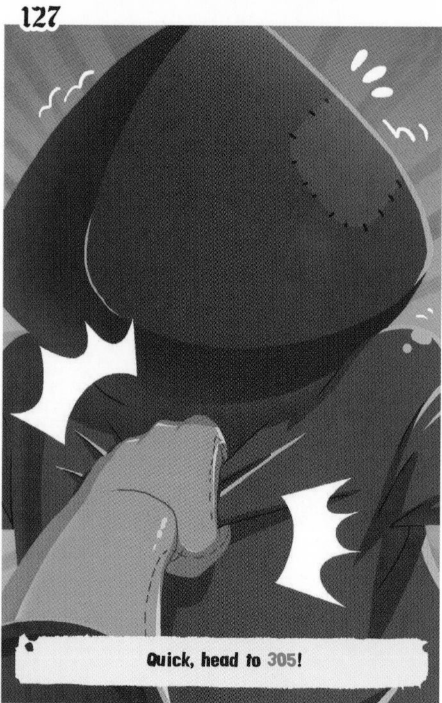

Quick, head to 305!

128

This poor guy fell into a trap set by the Patikas, the terrible inhabitants of this island. Best not to hang around long. Get back to the boat by following the path at 36.

129

INDEED, I HAVE MY OWN IDEAS ON THE MATTER. I VERY MUCH APPRECIATE THE CULTURE OF THE MOOSE, THE INHABITANTS OF JENOVA ISLAND. I'M RATHER INTRIGUED BY IT, ACTUALLY. WOULD YOU BELIEVE THAT WANOSH, THE ONCE GREAT SORCERER, ADORED ANIMALS? IN FACT, HE SCULPTED MANY TOTEMS IN THEIR IMAGE. I THINK WE SHOULD DIG ON THIS SIDE.
You can now return to 240.

130

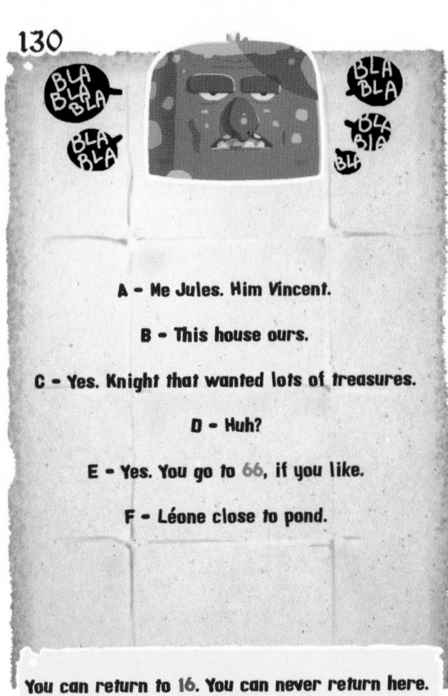
BLA BLA BLA
BLA BLA
BLA BLA
A - Me Jules. Him Vincent.
B - This house ours.
C - Yes. Knight that wanted lots of treasures.
D - Huh?
E - Yes. You go to 66, if you like.
F - Léone close to pond.
You can return to 16. You can never return here.

131

If you're tired of walking around this island, you can get back on your boat and return to the sea at page 2.
170
347
4=I
35

132

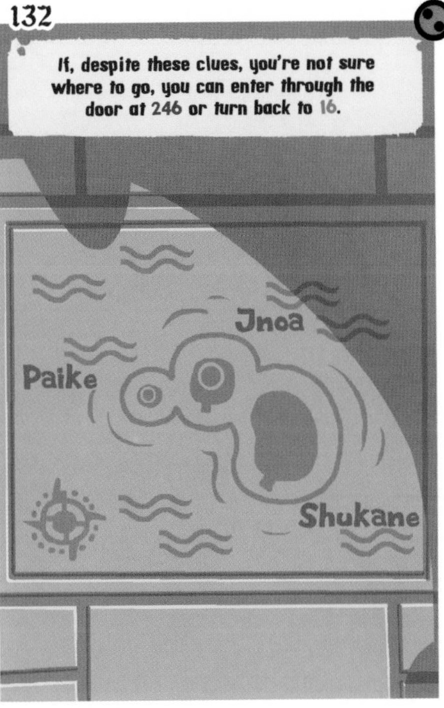
If, despite these clues, you're not sure where to go, you can enter through the door at 246 or turn back to 16.
Jnoa
Paike
Shukane

133

If you think that this is Jasmine's son, go to 345. If you think he is Mrs. Lichpountaineger's son, go to 98. If you no idea who his mother might be, go to 84.

134

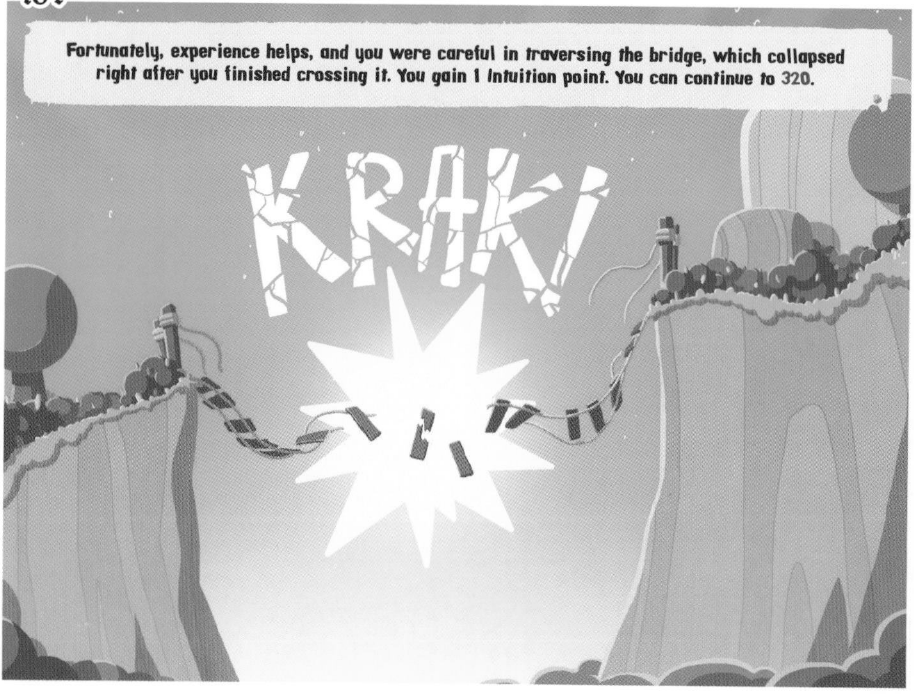

Fortunately, experience helps, and you were careful in traversing the bridge, which collapsed right after you finished crossing it. You gain 1 Intuition point. You can continue to 320.

KRAK!

135

AH HECK, OF COURSE! COME QUICK TO 83, PIRATE. WE'RE HEADED TO THE HARBOR! I KNOW SOMEONE WHO WILL LEND YOU A BOAT SO YOU CAN GO TO JENOVA ISLAND.
YIPPEE KI YAY!

136

ELLIOT? A CROOK IF THERE EVER WAS ONE... HE OWES ME 12 GOLD PIECES! I BET YOU'RE IN CAHOOTS WITH EM, TOO, SCOUNDREL! GET OUTTA MY INN, SCALLYWAG, AND RETURN TO 147!

137

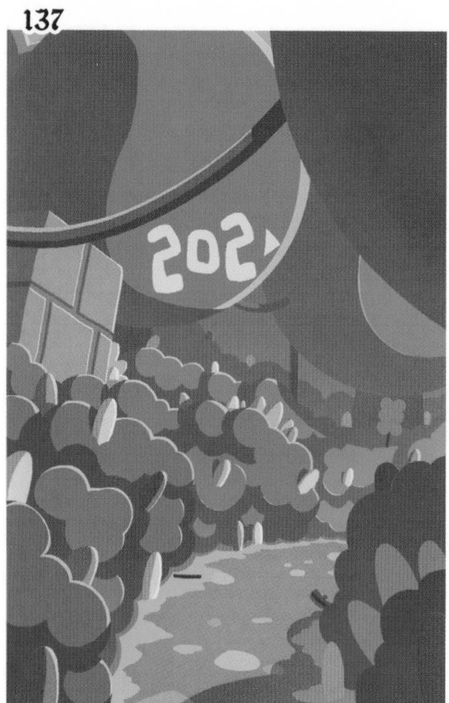
202

138

Go to 89 to stop this fugitive in his tracks and question him.

139

The rock was a step too far. The shaman will obliterate you with a single blow... You're dead and can restart your adventure on page 2.

140

WHAT A WASTE OF TIME! YOU REALLY DON'T HAVE ANY IDEA WHAT YOU'RE DOING, DO YOU? JUST GO TO 163 ALREADY!

141

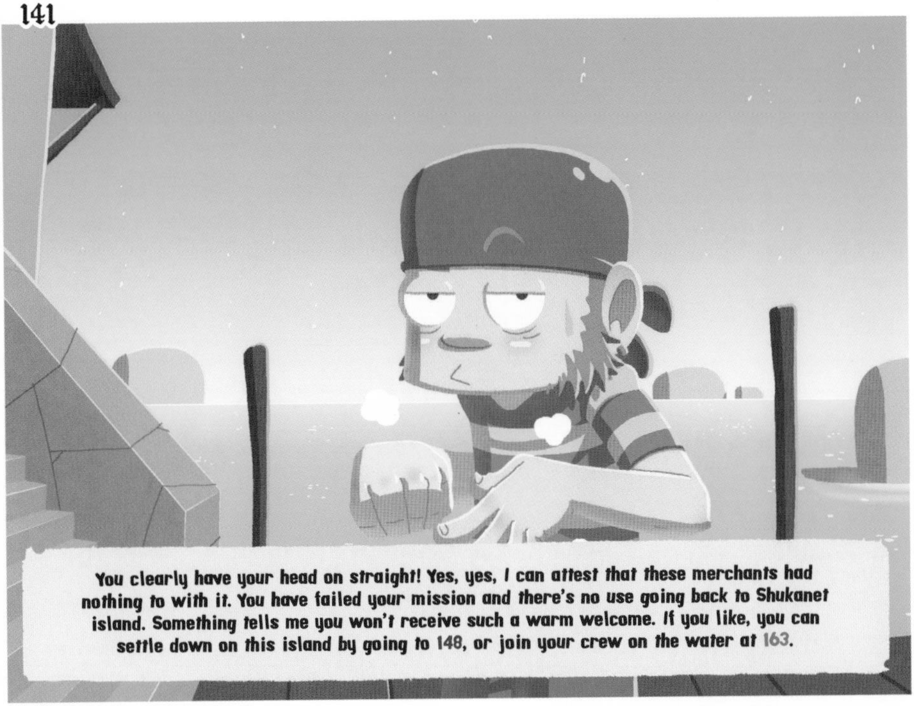

You clearly have your head on straight! Yes, yes, I can attest that these merchants had nothing to with it. You have failed your mission and there's no use going back to Shukanet island. Something tells me you won't receive such a warm welcome. If you like, you can settle down on this island by going to 148, or join your crew on the water at 163.

142

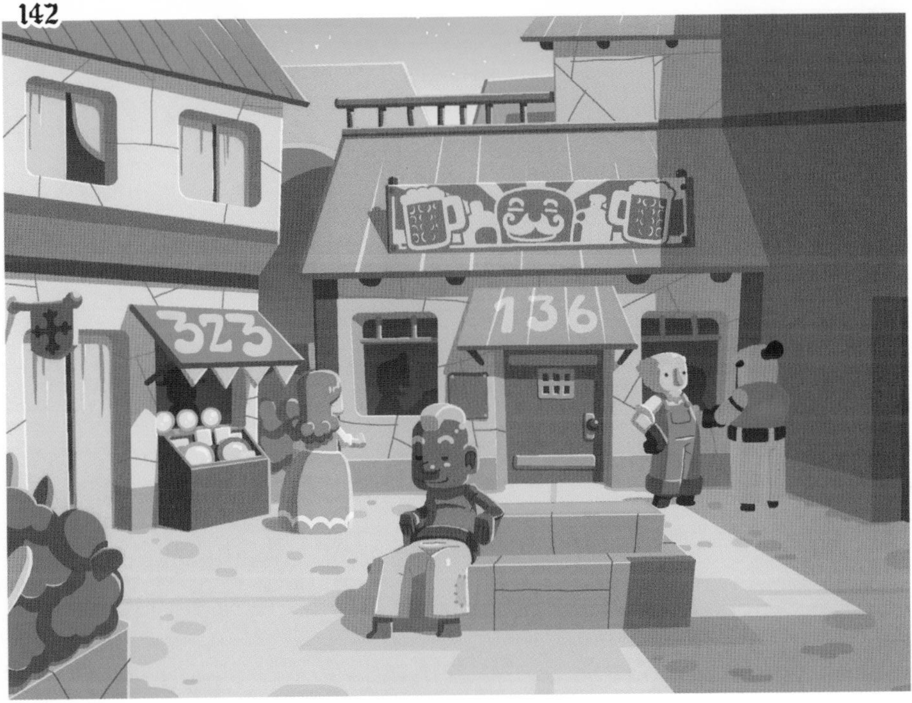

323

136

143

If you have more than 10 Intuition or Intelligence, or if you are younger than 13, go to 180.

144

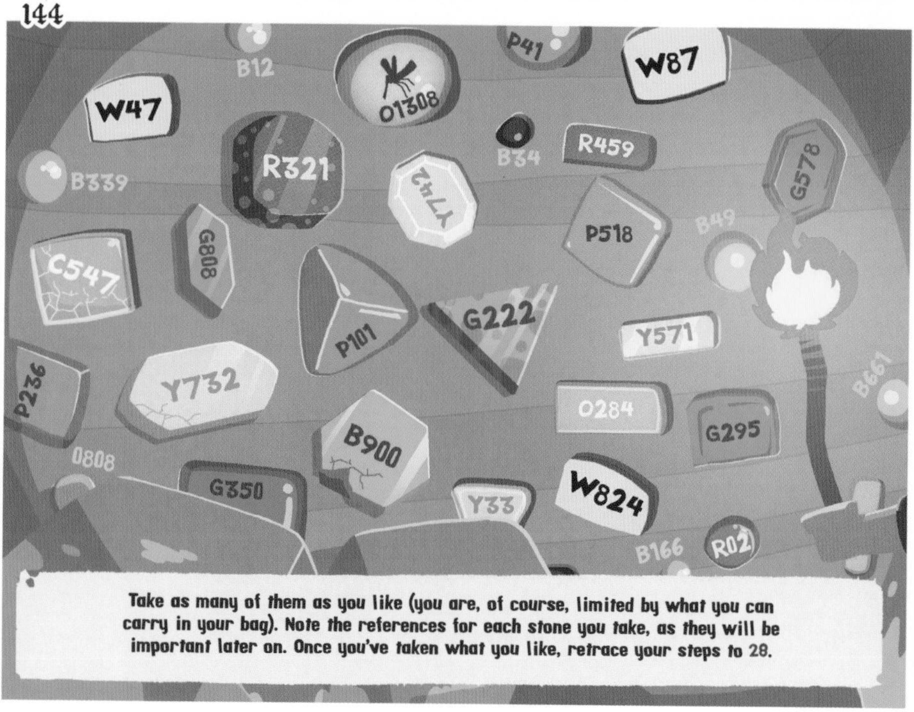

Take as many of them as you like (you are, of course, limited by what you can carry in your bag). Note the references for each stone you take, as they will be important later on. Once you've taken what you like, retrace your steps to 28.

145

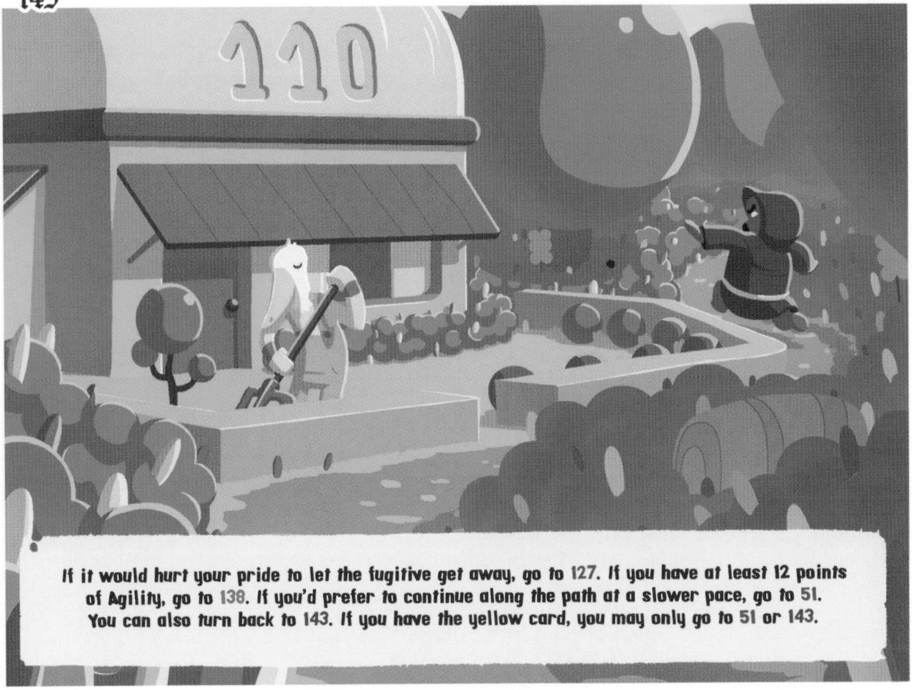

If it would hurt your pride to let the fugitive get away, go to 127. If you have at least 12 points of Agility, go to 138. If you'd prefer to continue along the path at a slower pace, go to 51. You can also turn back to 143. If you have the yellow card, you may only go to 51 or 143.

146

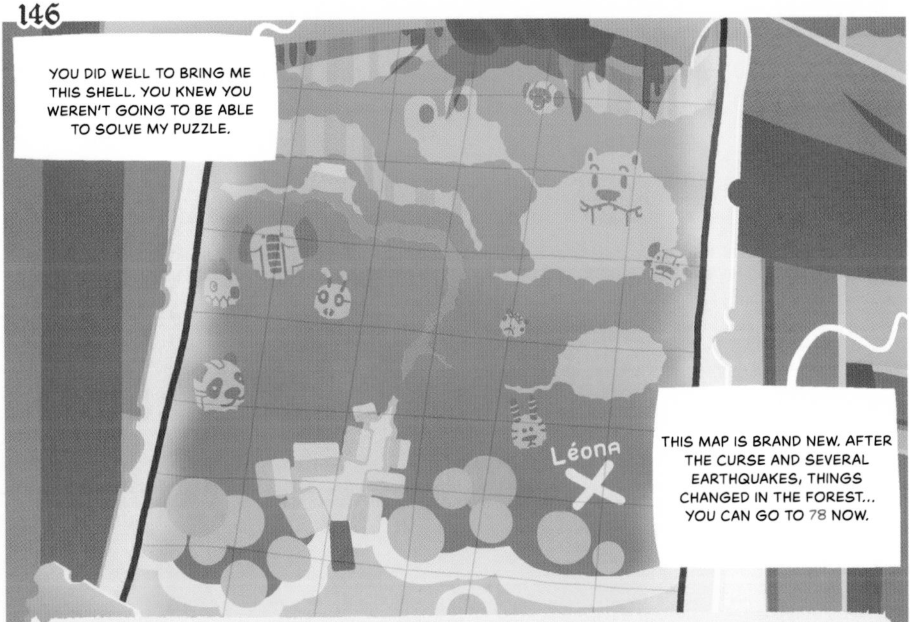

YOU DID WELL TO BRING ME THIS SHELL. YOU KNEW YOU WEREN'T GOING TO BE ABLE TO SOLVE MY PUZZLE.

THIS MAP IS BRAND NEW. AFTER THE CURSE AND SEVERAL EARTHQUAKES, THINGS CHANGED IN THE FOREST... YOU CAN GO TO 78 NOW.

Make sure to note the number of this panel, so you can come look at this map anytime.

147

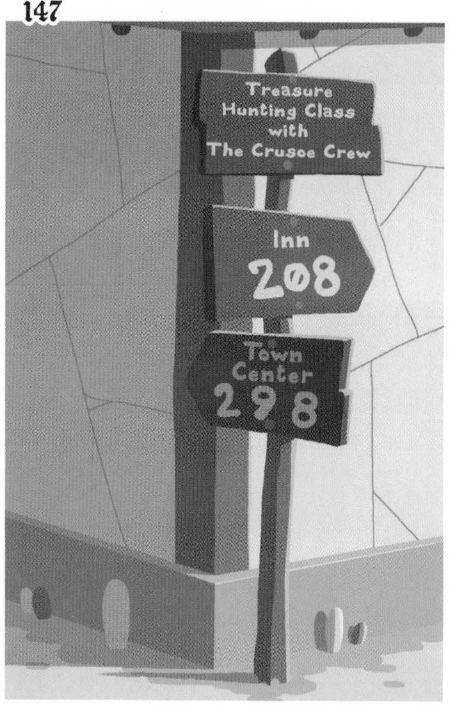
Treasure Hunting Class with The Crusoe Crew
Inn
208
Town Center
298

148

Look on the bright side: you can live out your days surrounded by friends. They all ended up here thanks to their missions, too. Or you can restart your adventure on page 2.

149

HOW LUCKY WE ARE TO HAVE FOUND YOU! YOUR DETERMINATION IS INSPIRING. HOWEVER, I RECOMMEND THAT YOU PASS BY JENOVA ISLAND BEFORE RUSHING HEADLONG TO ONE OF THE BOATS, AS EACH OF THE REGIONS ON THAT MAP ARE A THOUSAND MILES FROM HERE. WHO KNOWS WHAT COULD HAPPEN IF YOU END UP GOING TO THE WRONG PLACE... YOU UNDERSTAND WHAT I'M GETTING AT, RIGHT?
If heeding the advice of some big stuffed toy isn't your style, take to the sea at 241, but take care to identify and memorize the coat of arms of the boat you wish to follow. If you'd prefer to be cautious, go to 221. If, for whatever reason, you've decided against pursuing this whole boat theory, head to 125. Or if you're suddenly doubting the boat you chose, go to 287.

150

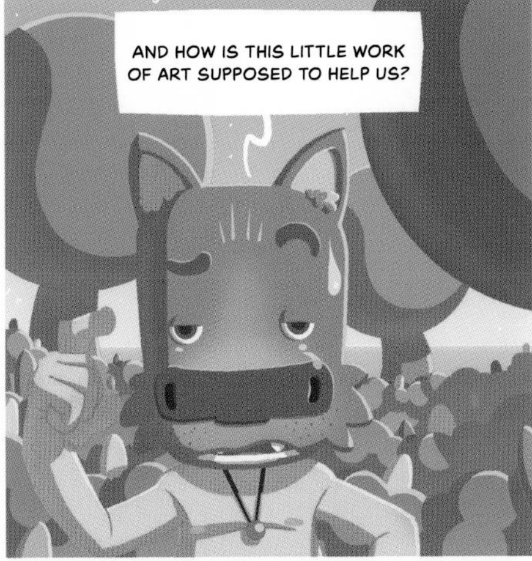
AND HOW IS THIS LITTLE WORK OF ART SUPPOSED TO HELP US?

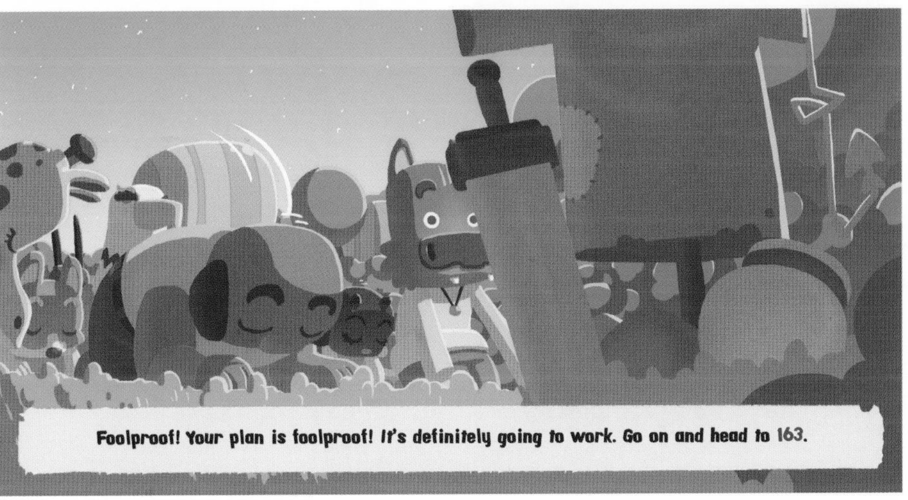
Foolproof! Your plan is foolproof! It's definitely going to work. Go on and head to 163.

151

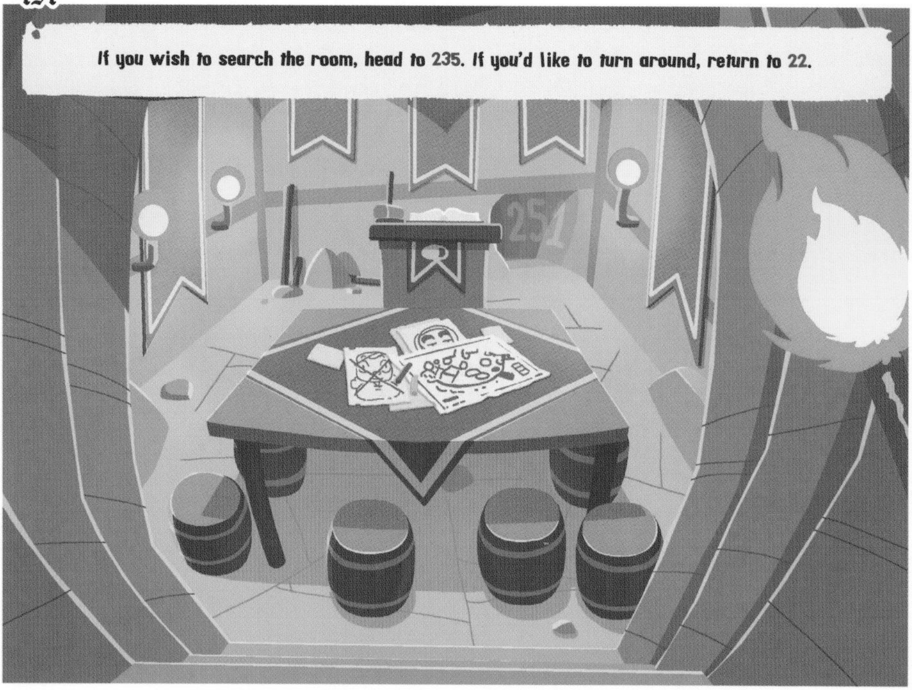

If you wish to search the room, head to 235. If you'd like to turn around, return to 22.

152

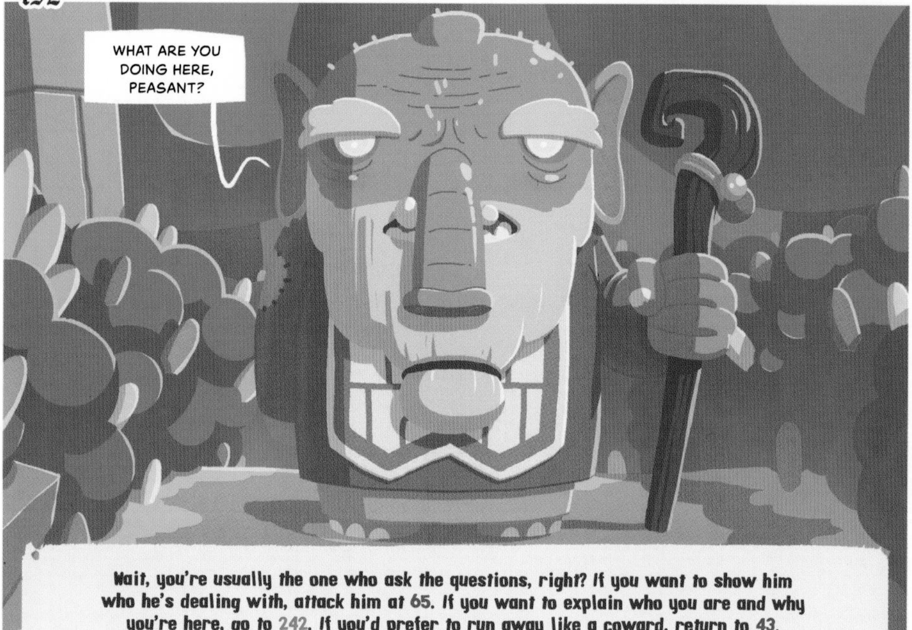

WHAT ARE YOU DOING HERE, PEASANT?

Wait, you're usually the one who ask the questions, right? If you want to show him who he's dealing with, attack him at 65. If you want to explain who you are and why you're here, go to 242. If you'd prefer to run away like a coward, return to 43.

153

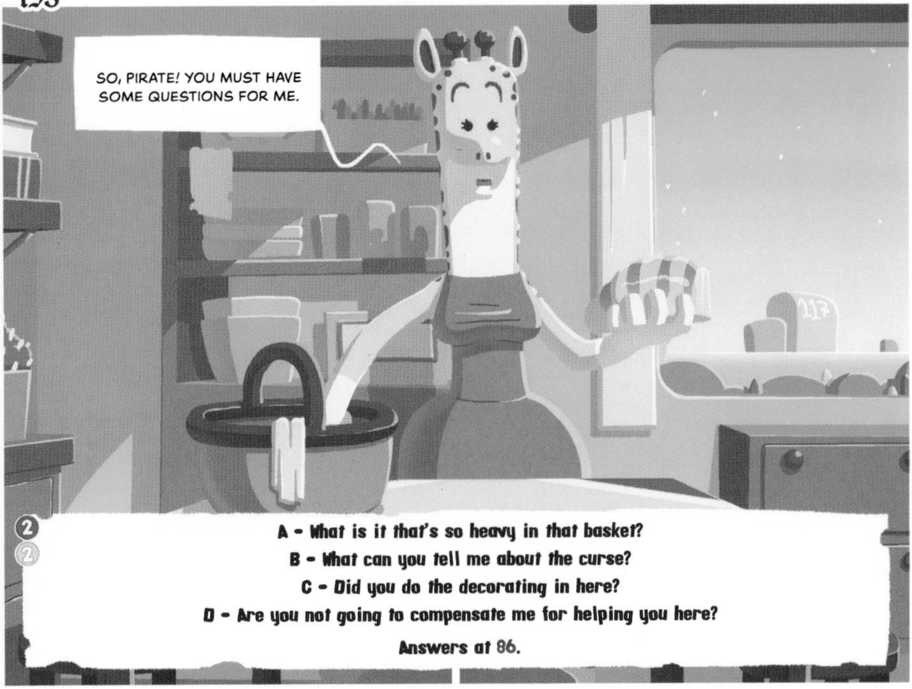

SO, PIRATE! YOU MUST HAVE SOME QUESTIONS FOR ME.

A - What is it that's so heavy in that basket?

B - What can you tell me about the curse?

C - Did you do the decorating in here?

D - Are you not going to compensate me for helping you here?

Answers at 86.

154

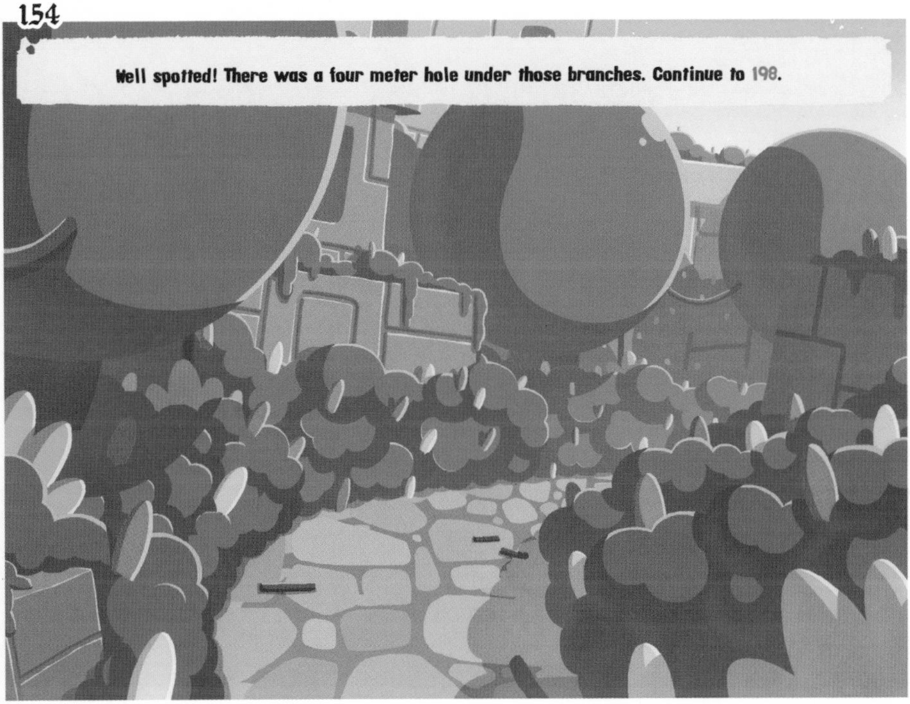

Well spotted! There was a four meter hole under those branches. **Continue to 198.**

155

WHAT'S HAPPENING? WHAT DO YOU WANT NOW?
WE KNOW YOUR SECRET, JASMINE... WE KNOW YOU'RE RESPONSIBLE FOR THE CURSE THAT HANGS OVER THIS VILLAGE!

Go to 123 to witness the reaction of this awful sorceress!

156

342

157

BLA BLA BLA
BLA BLA
BLA BLA
BLA

A - No idea, but they were rude enough to throw a cake in my flowers!

B - He's quite discreet, and I respect that. I'll give you one hint: find his first name and you'll be able to enter.

C - Flowers, vegetables... that sort of thing.

D - Well, I've been living on this island for about 10 years. I enjoy the climate, the serenity, and the people.

E - He's a quiet man, discreet, sweet. But he hasn't left his house since the curse hit. Who knows what he transformed into...

F - Hmm... It's not impossible. There are plenty of secrets, gossip, and other strange things in this village.

You can return to 145.

158

If you have more than 13 agility or fewer than 10 objects in your bag, you can climb a little higher to 299. You can remove objects from your bag if you like, but you won't be able to retrieve them later.

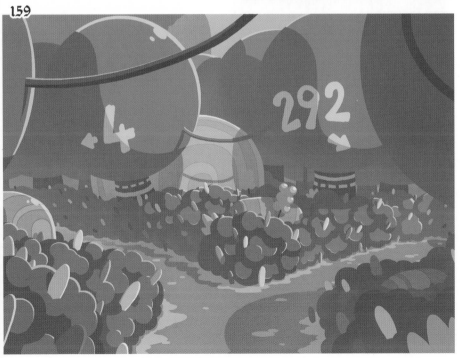

159

4

292

160

If you see a book that interests you, read it. Or do you not like reading? If that's the case, I just want to remind you that the thing you're holding in your hands right now is called a book... Once you think you've seen everything you need to see here, you can leave the city and return to 16. You cannot return here for the rest of your adventure.

Wanosh the Great
CONSTANTINE
ONE PIECE
CERISE
SUPER MAN
GREEN LANTERN
RING CIRCUS
NARUTO
HANA ATTORE
LUCHA LIBRE
HULK
SKY DOLL
The Descendants of Wanosh
Natanel We Love You
D.E.R.O.
AGITO COSMOS
HELLBOY
NORMAN
ZULU COPS
Ratafia
KATZ
Making Jam in Three Lessons

161

No need to talk to that dog... All the people here actually look human. Now go find Elliot, the merchant.

PAPA
OCTO
147
MAMA
HEN

162

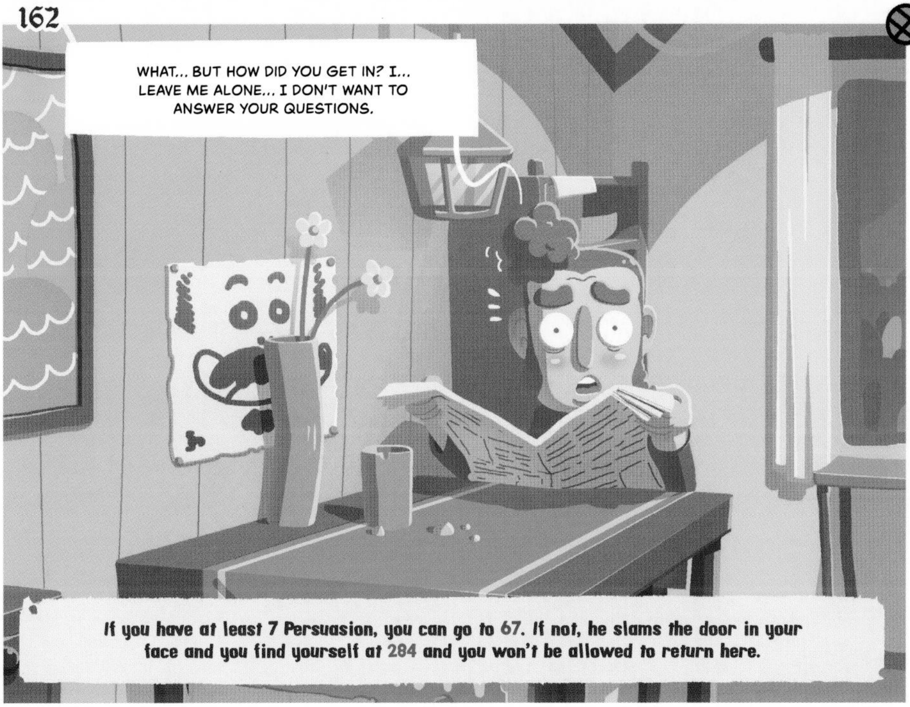

WHAT... BUT HOW DID YOU GET IN? I... LEAVE ME ALONE... I DON'T WANT TO ANSWER YOUR QUESTIONS.

If you have at least 7 Persuasion, you can go to 67. If not, he slams the door in your face and you find yourself at 284 and you won't be allowed to return here.

163

Here ends the formidable adventure of Pirates – The Cursed Isle.

After all, we're pirates, what were they expecting?

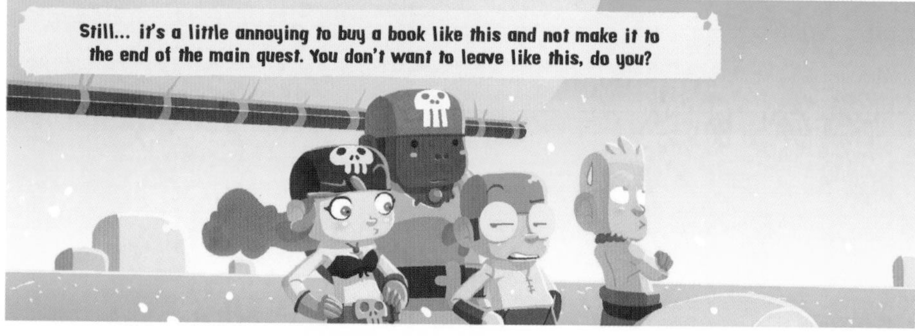
Still... it's a little annoying to buy a book like this and not make it to the end of the main quest. You don't want to leave like this, do you?

Go on, do me a favor, restart the adventure by turning back to page 2. And yes, just in case it wasn't crystal clear, you didn't end up helping the people of that island.

164

A - What do you do for work?

B - What can you tell me about the curse?

C - Is there anyone you think might know more than others about the curse?

D - I found these red stones. Can you tell me anything about them? (You may only ask this question if you possess the red volcanic stones.)

E - The last time, you told me that it was right under your nose? Why? (You may only ask this question if you had previously asked Maurice about the curse.)

F - Can you tell me exactly which island you were talking about last time? (You may only ask this question if you had previously asked Maurice about the red stones.)

Answers at 267.

165

BLA BLA BLA
BLA BLA
BLA BLA

A - Going for a walk, you?

B - My name's Kevin.

C - You can find her on the path by the pond.

D - In the opposite direction. Best to turn around and head to 43.

E - Oh yes, several! They're beautiful, eh?

You can continue to 230 or turn back to 43.

166

Two days have passed. You're hungrier than you've ever been. If you had any fishing equipment, it seems to be lost now. If you have more than 15 Agility, you manage to catch some fish with your bare hands. Otherwise, you lose 1 Strength point. But look on the bright side, the sun isn't as unbearable as it was yesterday. You can continue on your route to 13 or you can try to return to the Shukanet harbor at 217.

167

Dagnabbit, that was dumb! The vase makes thunderous noise as it falls. Run to 218, and fast.

168

Did you really think you would have a peaceful walk through the forest? Go to 105 to see how many bones you have left intact.

169

277

170

If you're sick of walking in circles on this island, you can get back on your boat and return to the seas on page 2.
131
35

171

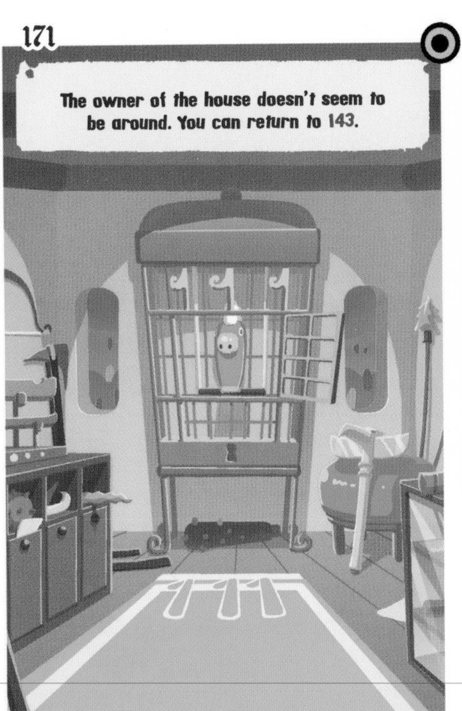
The owner of the house doesn't seem to be around. You can return to 143.

172

329.

173

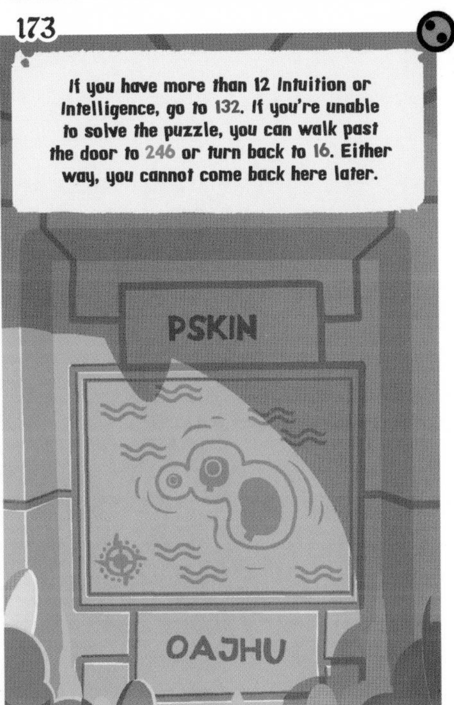
If you have more than 12 Intuition or Intelligence, go to 132. If you're unable to solve the puzzle, you can walk past the door to 246 or turn back to 16. Either way, you cannot come back here later.
PSKIN
OAJHU

174

Clearly, you asked the wrong question. Return from whence you came.

175

I'M SURE YOU'RE A FINE PIRATE, BUT YOU ARE A TRULY AWFUL INVESTIGATOR. YOU CAN LEAVE THE VILLAGE BY GOING TO 163.

176

A - What are you doing here?
B - Who are you?
C - Where can I find Léona, the forest girl?
D - Where can I find the buried city?
E - Are there other totems in this direction?
Answers at 165.

177

1-1-4-7-4-7
332
234
285

178

Dry yourself off, remove the soil from your ears, and follow the route to 198.
198

179
IT WASHN'T MUH... I PROMISH YUH I DIDN'T... I FOUND IT ON THE GROUND... I...
A - We know you're responsible for the curse... tell us everything!
B - What do we have to do to lift the curse?
C - You're poisoning cakes, is that it?
D - Talk, scoundrel, or I'll show you what a pirate is capable of!
Answers at 201.
180
Concentrate on the last word. Which digits end in the letter T? The answer to that will tell you what the other four symbols in that word are, which will tell you what some of the symbols are and aren't in the first word.
What if you think back to connect-the-dot puzzles you would do as a child. Don't lose sight of what you're looking for.
284
X=T
TT
No but, seriously, you're not even trying... you shouldn't need a hint to understand that you need to just go to panel 284!
The answer might be found in one of the neighboring houses.

181

60

182

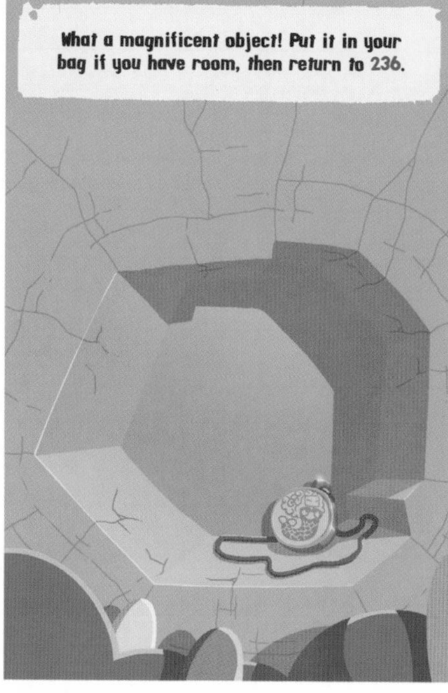
What a magnificent object! Put it in your bag if you have room, then return to 236.

183

WELL... COME NOW... UHH... WE'RE ALL GOOD PEOPLE HERE, NO NEED TO ARGUE. KEEP THIS TO YOURSELVES, AND I'LL FORGET ABOUT THAT LOUSY OLD VASE.
You can now return to 240.

184

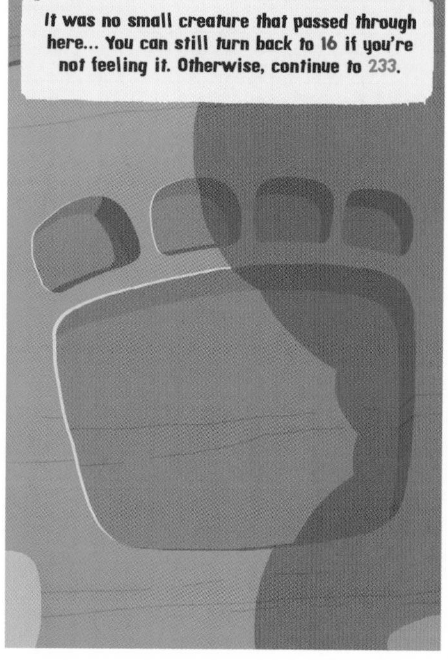
It was no small creature that passed through here... You can still turn back to 16 if you're not feeling it. Otherwise, continue to 233.

185

A - I... I WAS SCARED OF YOU... YOU HAVE TO ADMIT, YOU DON'T LOOK THAT FRIENDLY.

B - BECAUSE IT OFTEN RAINS AROUND HERE, AND I DON'T LIKE HAVING WET FUR. IT'S RATHER UNPLEASANT.

C - OH, FROM THERE... I WAS WALKING.

D - I'M SURE THAT JASMINE IS INVOLVED SOMEHOW. SHE'S HIDING A TERRIBLE SECRET, THAT MUCH IS CERTAIN.

E - PICKING APPLES. MRS. LICHPOUNTAINEGER IS MAKING AN APPLE PIE, AND SHE ASKED ME TO FIND SOME.

F - ABSOLUTELY NOT.

You can retrace your steps in 143, continue straight on 51 or, if you have more than 5 Intuition, you can ask more questions on 273.

186

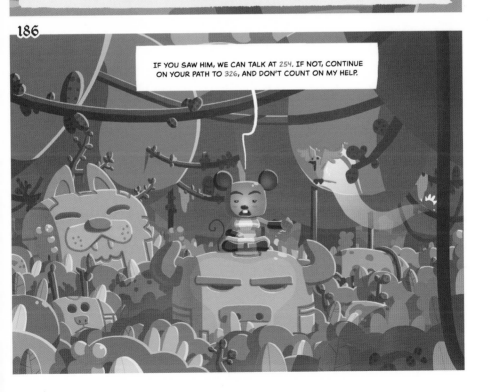

IF YOU SAW HIM, WE CAN TALK AT 254. IF NOT, CONTINUE ON YOUR PATH TO 326, AND DON'T COUNT ON MY HELP.

187

A - Might you have a map of the sky, so that we can learn more about the curse?

B - Are you with me in thinking that the moon and the stars might be the cause of this curse?

C - I saw a telescope upstairs last time. Have you observed anything peculiar recently? (You may only ask this question if you have been to this house before.)

D - Maurice told me that you have an interesting theory about the curse. (You may only say this if Maurice told you about George's theory.)

E - Have you lived in this house a long time?

F - It smells good, are you cooking something?

Answers at 115.

THE MOON? COME ON...
CURIOUS THEORY.

188

189

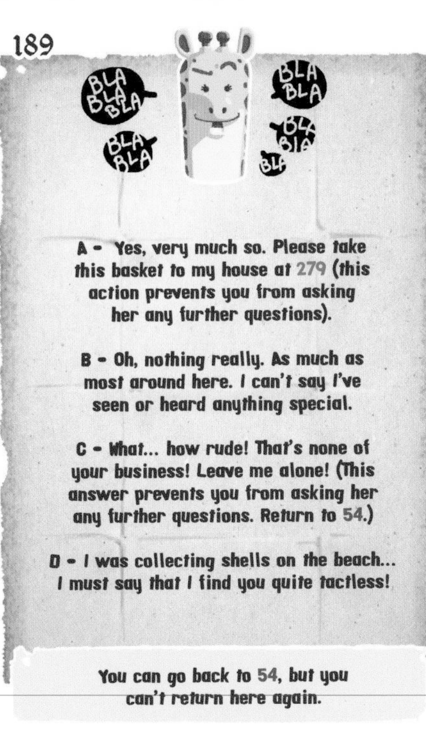
BLA BLA BLA
BLA BLA
BLA BLA
BLA BLA
BLA
A - Yes, very much so. Please take this basket to my house at 279 (this action prevents you from asking her any further questions).
B - Oh, nothing really. As much as most around here. I can't say I've seen or heard anything special.
C - What... how rude! That's none of your business! Leave me alone! (This answer prevents you from asking her any further questions. Return to 54.)
D - I was collecting shells on the beach... I must say that I find you quite tactless!
You can go back to 54, but you can't return here again.

190

233
184

191

Well done! Maurice agrees to speak with you at 164. However, if you failed to arrive at this answer, it's time to go. To 39!

192

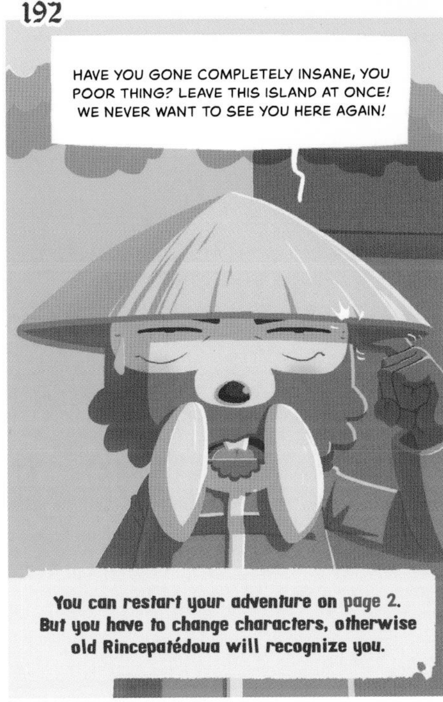
HAVE YOU GONE COMPLETELY INSANE, YOU POOR THING? LEAVE THIS ISLAND AT ONCE! WE NEVER WANT TO SEE YOU HERE AGAIN!
You can restart your adventure on page 2. But you have to change characters, otherwise old Rincepatédoua will recognize you.

193

309

194

239

195

23
211
72

196

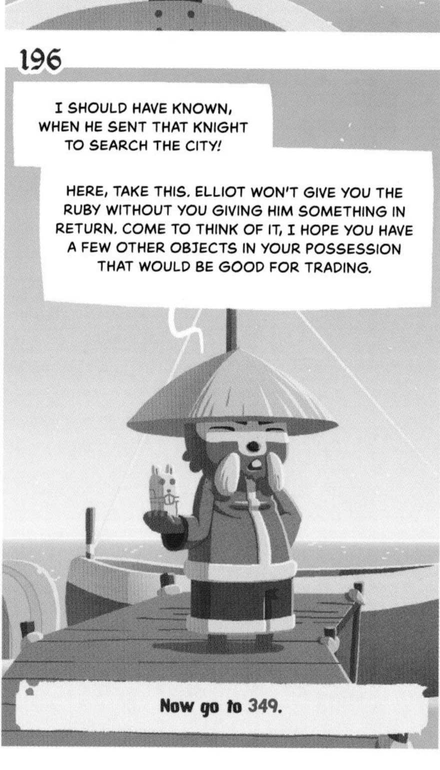
I SHOULD HAVE KNOWN, WHEN HE SENT THAT KNIGHT TO SEARCH THE CITY!
HERE, TAKE THIS. ELLIOT WON'T GIVE YOU THE RUBY WITHOUT YOU GIVING HIM SOMETHING IN RETURN. COME TO THINK OF IT, I HOPE YOU HAVE A FEW OTHER OBJECTS IN YOUR POSSESSION THAT WOULD BE GOOD FOR TRADING.
Now go to 349.

197

181
ENINYTH
GIEDRED
NUHØWT

198

308

199

200

One could say *that* the residents of the village owe you a debt of gratitude. Thanks to you, the curse will certainly be lifted. You decide to say your goodbyes and head to 124.

201

BLA BLA BLA
BLA BLA
BLA BLA
BLA BLA
BLA

A - What are you talking about? I didn't do anything, it's not my fault! I just love food, that's it!

B - How am I supposed to know? What do you take me for? Some kind of saint?

C - The cakes? Oh no, which ones? Are you telling me that I'm going to get sick?

D - I'm happy to talk to you, but what exactly do you want me to say?

These answers are hardly conclusive, and your Intuition (regardless of the stat number) is telling you to be suspicious of him. By the way, the chief wants to speak with you at his house. Go to 278.

202

169

You can cut these vines with a knife or a saber, if you have one. If not, you can always tear them with your bare hands, but you become exhausted and lose 1 Strength point. Either way, go to 268.

203

BLA BLA BLA
BLA BLA

BLA BLA
BLA BLA
BLA

A - Well that, I have no idea. On the plus side, I can fly, which makes me more discreet than before.

B - Apparently, yes.

C - I'm fairly certain that we aren't responsible for the curse. Everyone is appreciative and respectful in this village, and no one dislikes us enough to curse us.

D - From all over. I am... a bit of a collector. I like searching for rare objects. My most beautiful pieces are from Jenova Island.

E - Yes, in a more or less flagrant fashion. Some are so embarrassed that they refuse to leave their houses, like Tom, who lives in a house a little further down on the left.

F - Jasmine? No... who are you talking about?

You can now return to 143.

204

71

205

BLA BLA BLA
BLA BLA
BLA BLA
BLA BLA BLA

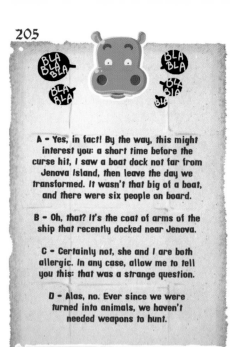

A - Yes, in fact! By the way, this might interest you: a short time before the curse hit, I saw a boat dock not far from Jenova Island, then leave the day we transformed. It wasn't that big of a boat, and there were six people on board.

B - Oh, that? It's the coat of arms of the ship that recently docked near Jenova.

C - Certainly not, she and I are both allergic. In any case, allow me to tell you this: that was a strange question.

D - Alas, no. Ever since we were turned into animals, we haven't needed weapons to hunt.

You can return to 240.

206

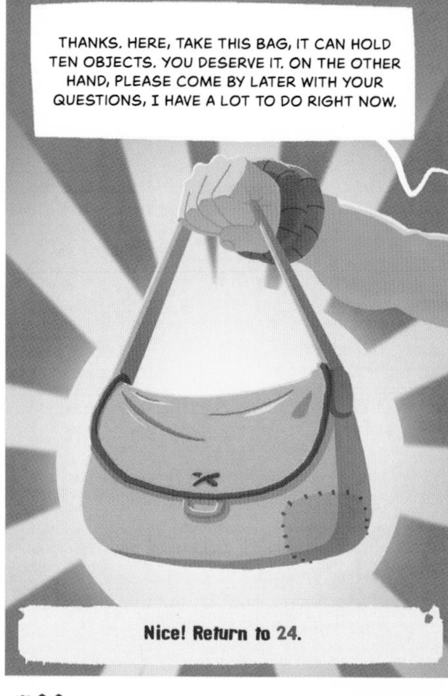

THANKS. HERE, TAKE THIS BAG, IT CAN HOLD TEN OBJECTS. YOU DESERVE IT. ON THE OTHER HAND, PLEASE COME BY LATER WITH YOUR QUESTIONS, I HAVE A LOT TO DO RIGHT NOW.

Nice! Return to 24.

207

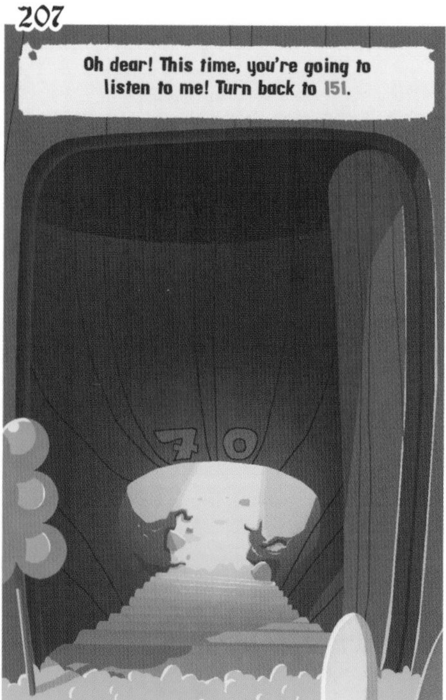

70

Oh dear! This time, you're going to listen to me! Turn back to 151.

208

142

And finally, calm, as far as the eye can see... It's time to admit that you're lost. No use sugar coating it, you're going to starve to death and then be eaten by sharks. You can restart your adventure on page 2.

Look closely, Elliot is hiding in this town! If you can't find him, you can turn back to 147. If you are younger than 13 years (or if you are suffering from Flemardus Papopulis Vanryderitus) and you're stumped, go to 280 for a few hints. Warning! The hints will make this much easier, which in turn could make your adventure less interesting. So don't go looking at the hints unless you are well and truly stumped.
THE MERCHANT? OF COURSE I KNOW HIM! HE'S EASY TO RECOGNIZE WITH HIS GOATEE, AND ESPECIALLY WITH THAT FUNNY THING ON HIS EYE...
HAVE YOU EVER BEEN TO ROME?
CCCC
MMI

211

119

212

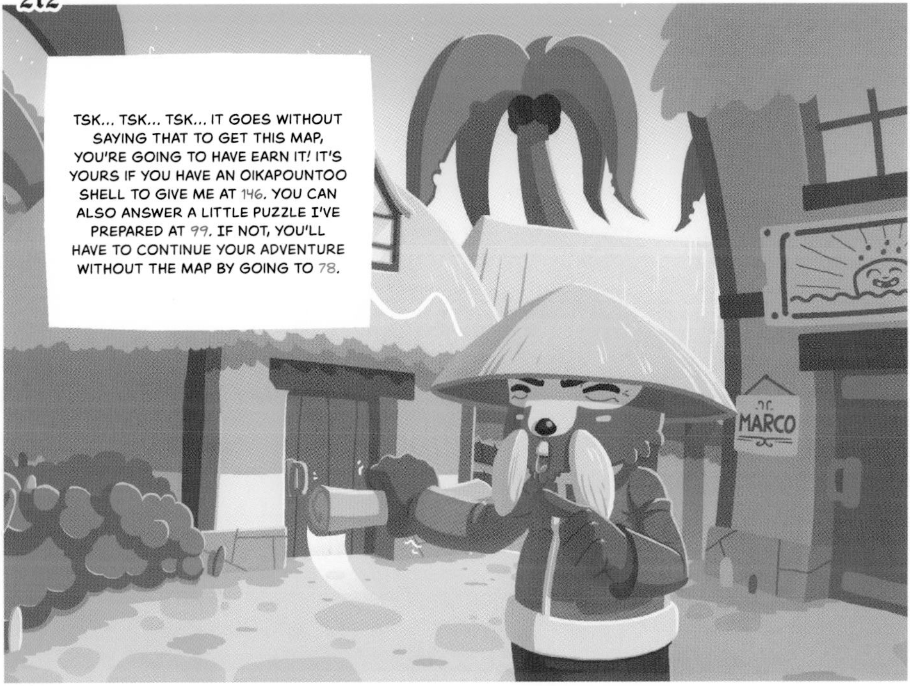

TSK... TSK... TSK... IT GOES WITHOUT SAYING THAT TO GET THIS MAP, YOU'RE GOING TO HAVE EARN IT! IT'S YOURS IF YOU HAVE AN OIKAPOUNTOO SHELL TO GIVE ME AT 146. YOU CAN ALSO ANSWER A LITTLE PUZZLE I'VE PREPARED AT 99. IF NOT, YOU'LL HAVE TO CONTINUE YOUR ADVENTURE WITHOUT THE MAP BY GOING TO 78.
MARCO

213

GO, PIRATE! YOU CAN EXPLORE THIS PART OF THE FOREST. BUT DON'T FORGET... IF YOU DON'T RESPECT IT, IT WILL PLAY TRICKS ON YOU.

156

So mysterious... Now go, let's go, are we going?

214

SO, PIRATE? DID YOU FIND ANY CLUES? DO YOU HAVE ANY LEADS? WHAT DO YOU WANT TO DO NOW?

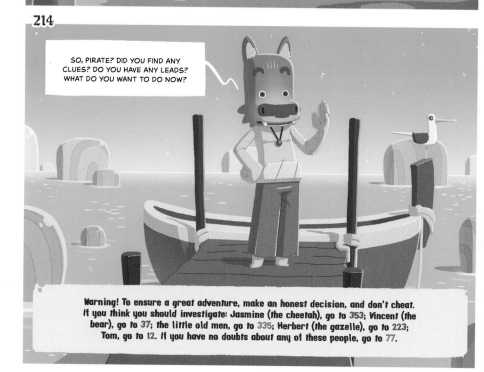

Warning! To ensure a *great adventure*, make an honest decision, and don't cheat. If you think you should investigate: Jasmine (the cheetah), go to 353; Vincent (the bear), go to 37; the little old men, go to 335; Herbert (the gazelle), go to 223; Tom, go to 12. If you have no doubts about any of these people, go to 77.

215

BLA BLA BLA
BLA BLA
BLA BLA
BLA BLA

A - We're getting some sun. You?

B - Julius and Marcus. We're the village elders.

C - Obviously. We've been here every day for... for a loooooong time, anyway!

D - Work? Y'aren't very observant for an investigator, kid! We haven't worked for a loooooong time.

E - Oh, me, if I were you, I'd take it, heh! Hehehe!

F - Isn't that what you're talking to us for?

G - We've been here a loooooong time.

H - Herbert? We know him well. He's been an odd one for some time now... like he's hiding something.

You can return to 303. However, you cannot interrogate these two charming little old men again.

216

TOM, OPEN UP, IT'S ESTEBAN, YOUR CHIEF! I'M ORDERING YOU TO OPEN THE DOOR!

Tom opens the door at 25.

217

It wasn't easy, but you succeed in returning to the island. The sheer exhaustion causes you to lose 1 point from each of your Characteristics. Esteban invites you to join him at 149, after you finish tending to your wounds.

BY THE GODS, PIRATE...

218

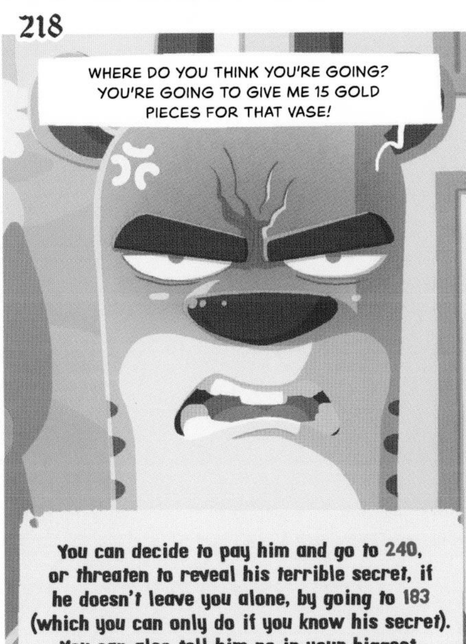

WHERE DO YOU THINK YOU'RE GOING? YOU'RE GOING TO GIVE ME 15 GOLD PIECES FOR THAT VASE!

You can decide to pay him and go to 240, or threaten to reveal his terrible secret, if he doesn't leave you alone, by going to 183 (which you can only do if you know his secret). You can also tell him no in your biggest, meanest, voice and go to 240, but only if you have more than 5 Persuasion points.

219

WELL, WELL, WHAT HAVE WE HERE? WE'RE NOT LETTING YOU GO THIS TIME, PIRATE! JEAN-MICHEL, GET THE POT BOILING. OUR MEAL HAS ARRIVED.
I'm afraid our carrots are cooked, my pirate friend! I guess this is what it all boils down to... Too bad! Go to page 2!

220

Such a warm welcome... Answers at 337.

DO NOT COME IN HERE! YOU CAN ASK YOUR QUESTIONS RIGHT HERE.

JASMiNE

1
2

A - Why can't we come in?
B - What do you do for work?
C - Do you live alone?
D - Do you know who might be able to help me?

221

TAKE THIS DINGY, THEN. HEAD SOUTH AND STOP AT PATIKAN ISLAND. THAT WAY, YOU'LL AVOID THE STRONG CURRENTS THAT WOULD DRAW YOU AWAY FROM THE SHORE. WHEN YOU DOCK, MAKE SURE TO LOOK FOR IDENTICAL SYMBOLS ENGRAVED ON THE TREES SO YOU DON'T GET LOST OR STUCK. THEN, YOU SHOULD FIND A SMALL RED AND WHITE BOAT OF MINE THAT WILL TAKE YOU TO JENOVA.
HERE'S 50 GOLD PIECES FOR YOUR EFFORTS.

All of this encouragement has motivated you, and you gain 2 *Intuition* points. Take to the sea at 112.

222

MY FRIENDS! WE HAVE THE EXTRAORDINARY PLEASURE OF WELCOMING THIS ADVENTURE TO OUR VILLAGE. THEY WILL LEAD THE INVESTIGATION TO DETERMINE THE CAUSE OF THE CURSE THAT HAS PLAGUED US FOR SO LONG. TO DO SO, THEY WILL GO FROM HOUSE TO HOUSE, LOOKING FOR CLUES AND INTERROGATING EACH ONE OF YOU. SPEAK CLEARLY, AS THEY WILL BE USING THEIR CHARACTER SHEET TO TAKE NOTE OF ANY DETAILS THAT SEEM IMPORTANT.
MEETING ADJOURNED.
PIRATE COME TO 26. THERE'S SOMETHING I SHOULD TELL YOU BEFORE YOU START.

223

YOU ARE DECIDEDLY THE WORST INVESTIGATOR THAT I HAVE EVER SEEN! WE NO LONGER NEED YOUR SERVICES. YOU CAN GO TO 163.

224

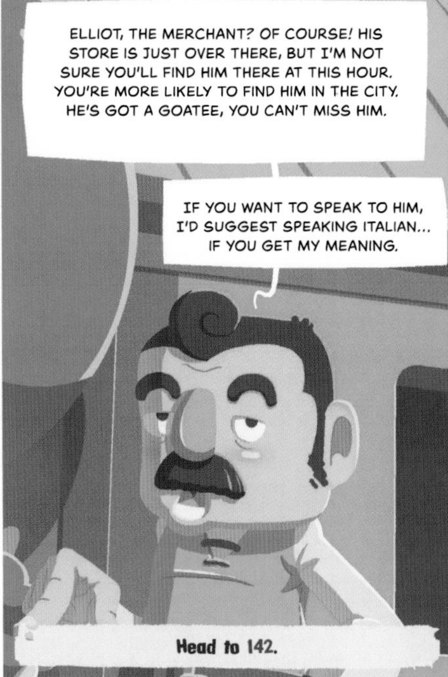
ELLIOT, THE MERCHANT? OF COURSE! HIS STORE IS JUST OVER THERE, BUT I'M NOT SURE YOU'LL FIND HIM THERE AT THIS HOUR. YOU'RE MORE LIKELY TO FIND HIM IN THE CITY. HE'S GOT A GOATEE, YOU CAN'T MISS HIM.
IF YOU WANT TO SPEAK TO HIM, I'D SUGGEST SPEAKING ITALIAN... IF YOU GET MY MEANING.

Head to 142.

225

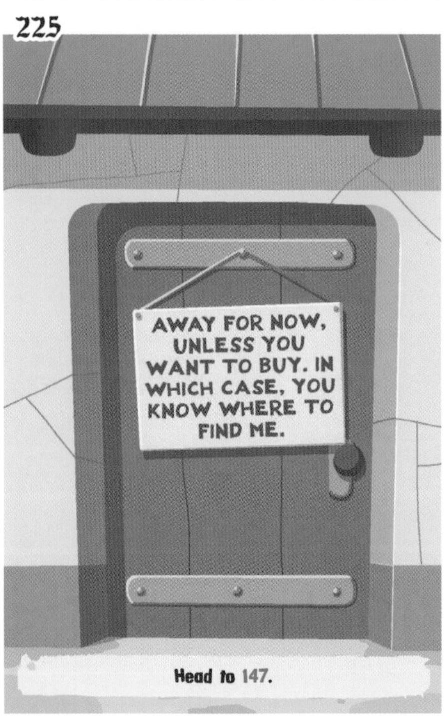
AWAY FOR NOW, UNLESS YOU WANT TO BUY. IN WHICH CASE, YOU KNOW WHERE TO FIND ME.

Head to 147.

226

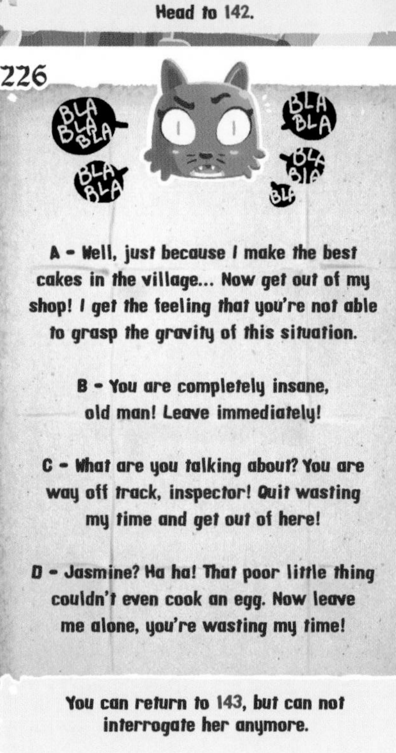
BLA BLA BLA
BLA BLA
BLA BLA
BLA BLA
BLA

A - Well, just because I make the best cakes in the village... Now get out of my shop! I get the feeling that you're not able to grasp the gravity of this situation.

B - You are completely insane, old man! Leave immediately!

C - What are you talking about? You are way off track, inspector! Quit wasting my time and get out of here!

D - Jasmine? Ha ha! That poor little thing couldn't even cook an egg. Now leave me alone, you're wasting my time!

You can return to 143, but can not interrogate her anymore.

227

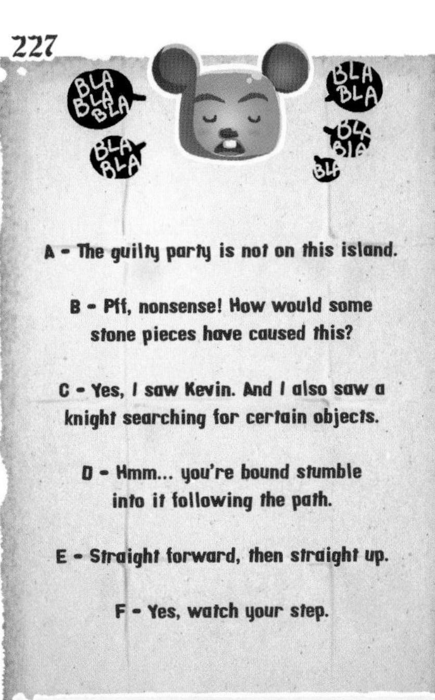
BLA BLA BLA
BLA BLA
BLA BLA
BLA BLA
BLA

A - The guilty party is not on this island.

B - Pff, nonsense! How would some stone pieces have caused this?

C - Yes, I saw Kevin. And I also saw a knight searching for certain objects.

D - Hmm... you're bound stumble into it following the path.

E - Straight forward, then straight up.

F - Yes, watch your step.

You can continue to 326.

228

A - I am Mrs. Lichpountaineger, and I've lived here since I was small. Now, please leave me be, I have cooking to do.

B - Well... I'm not sure. I had the impression that the sky got darker, but... that's all I remember.

C - Oh, yes! And it's even more beautiful from the end of a pontoon. My son, the village armorer, gazes at the horizon for hours.

D - No, I live with my son. He's the village armorer. He makes magnificent swords.

After hearing this adorable little granny's answer, return to 177.

229

3
39

230

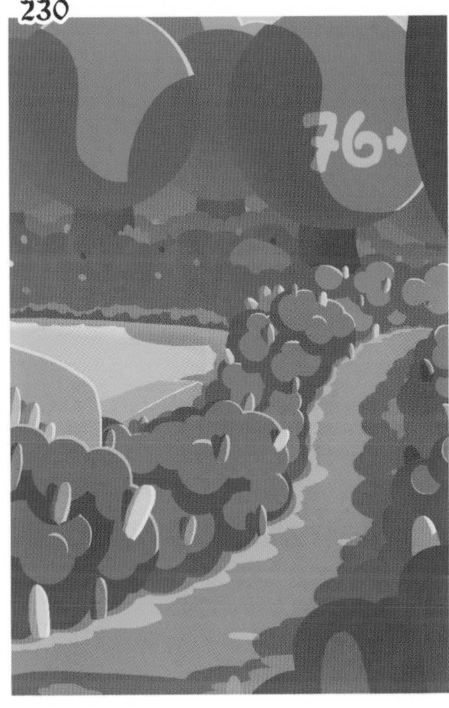
76

231

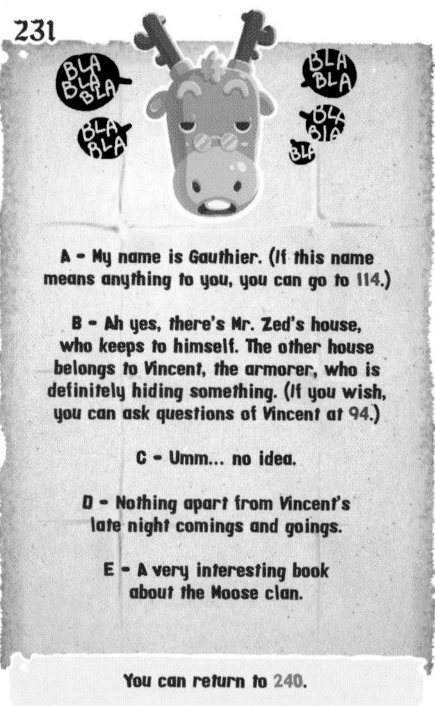
BLA BLA BLA
BLA BLA
BLA BLA
BLA BLA
BLA
A - My name is Gauthier. (If this name means anything to you, you can go to 114.)
B - Ah yes, there's Mr. Zed's house, who keeps to himself. The other house belongs to Vincent, the armorer, who is definitely hiding something. (If you wish, you can ask questions of Vincent at 94.)
C - Umm... no idea.
D - Nothing apart from Vincent's late night comings and goings.
E - A very interesting book about the Moose clan.
You can return to 240.

232

33

233

3
18

234

You can see the archipelago from here. It's quite nice. If cameras existed, you'd definitely snap a pic to send to your mom. You can return to 177.

235

You can return to 22.

236

If you have more than 12 Strength, and you wish to break this wall, go to 182.

85

344

237

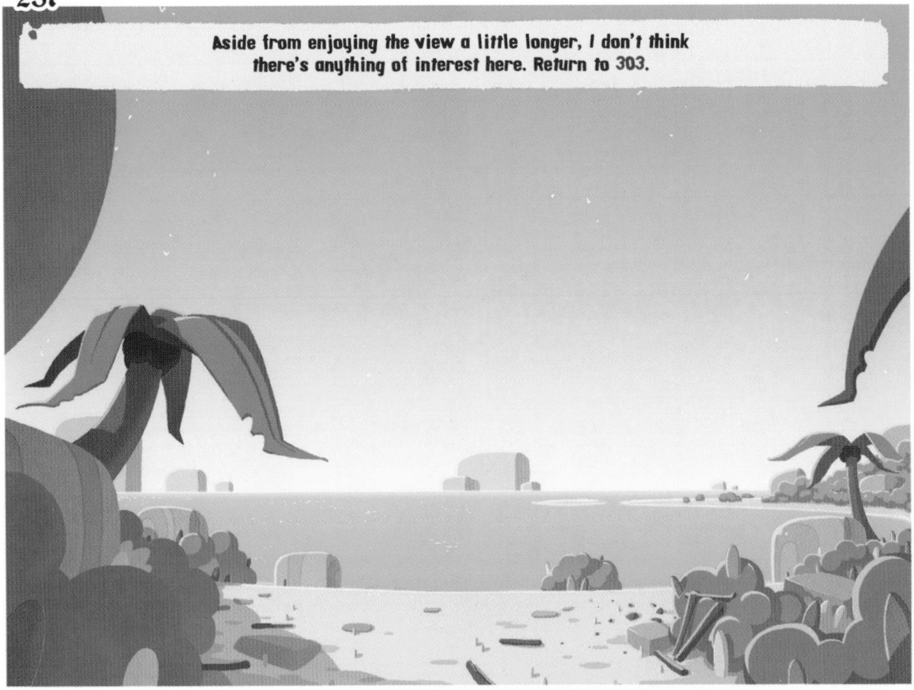

Aside from enjoying the view a little longer, I don't think there's anything of interest here. Return to 303.

238

CAN I HELP YOU? ELLIOT? YES, HE'S THE LITTLE MERCHANT WHO HAS A GOATEE AND ROMAN NUMERALS SHAPED LIKE A FISH ON HIS CLOTHES.

Return to 298.

239

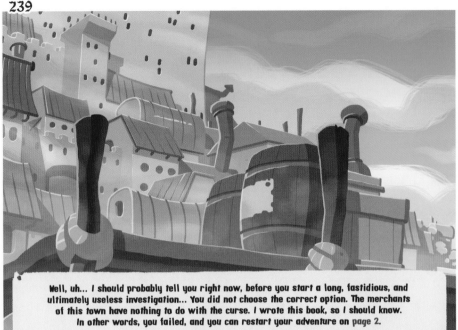

Well, uh... I should probably tell you right now, before you start a long, fastidious, and ultimately useless investigation... You did not choose the correct option. The merchants of this town have nothing to do with the curse. I wrote this book, so I should know. In other words, you failed, and you can restart your adventure on page 2.

240

4
6
133
SEA
75
265
Herbert
ZED
375
893
759

241

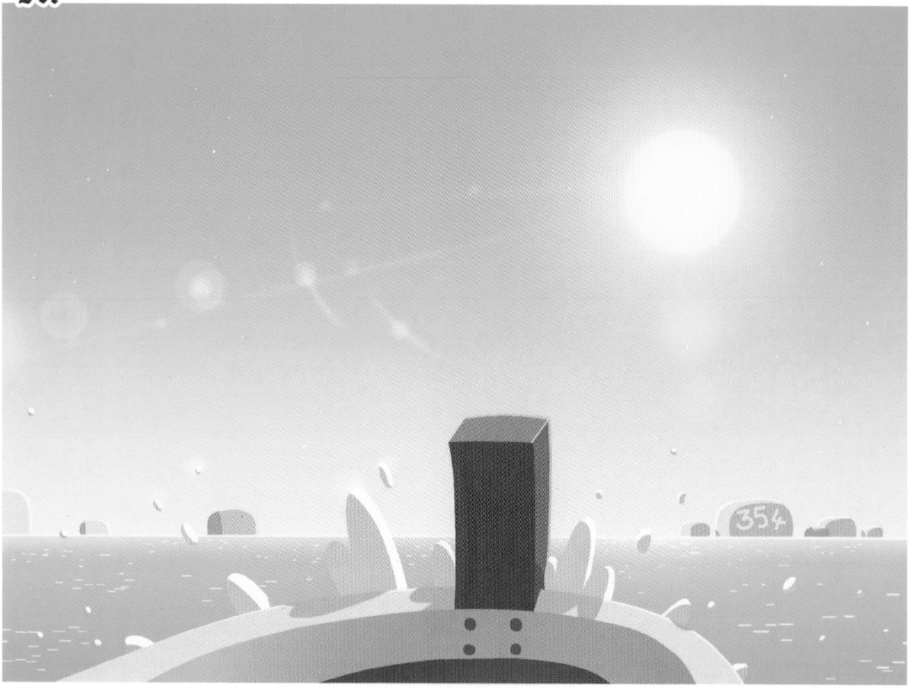

354

242

IT'S OF NO CONCERN TO ME, WORTHLESS PIRATE! I WILL ONLY ALLOW YOU TO PASS IF YOU PRESENT ME WITH A TIGER RING OR AN OCTOPUS NECKLACE. IF YOU HAVE ONE OF THESE, GO TO 213. OTHERWISE, TURN BACK TO 43.
What he doesn't mention is that you could also attack him at 65... he'll never see it coming!

243

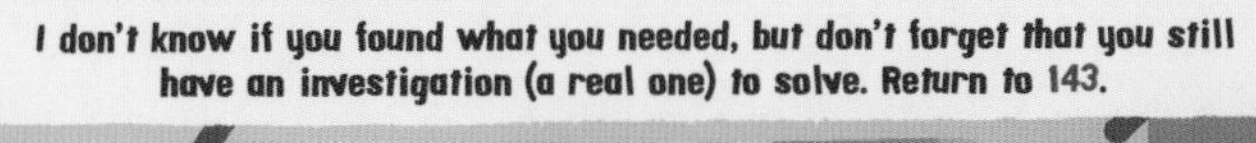
I don't know if you found what you needed, but don't forget that you still
have an investigation (a real one) to solve. Return to 143.

244

I'm afraid your employers will be slowly destroyed by the guardians of the city. You can restart your adventure on page 2.

245

A - What do you think of the book called Pirates: The Cursed Isle?
B - What did you do to curse the inhabitants of the Jenova archipelago?
C - I'm hungry, can you make me something to eat?
D - How can we remove the curse from the Jenova archipelago?

Answers at 7.

246

If you have at least 10 Intelligence or Intuition, go to 352. If you don't understand how you're supposed to enter, turn back and go to 16.

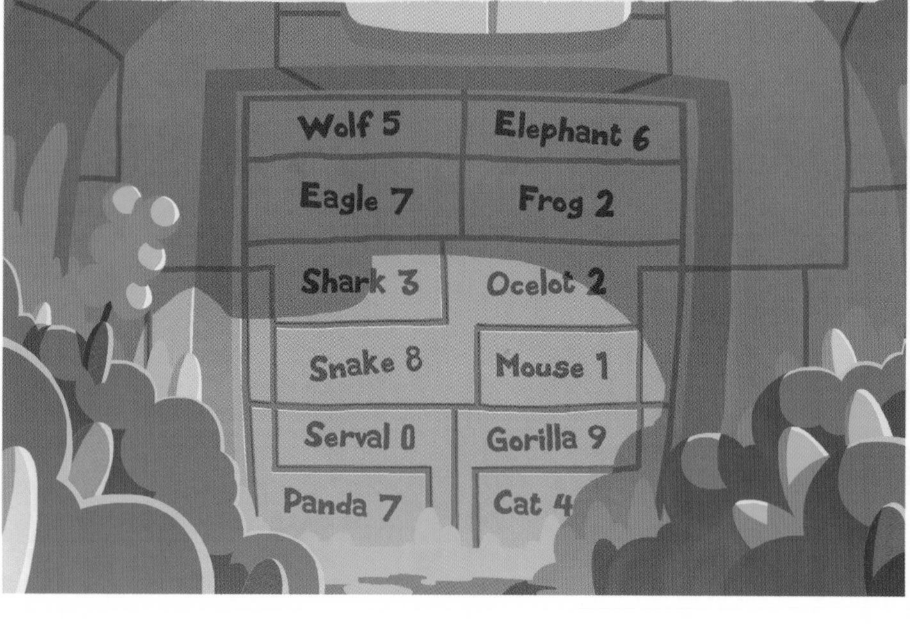

Wolf 5	Elephant 6
Eagle 7	Frog 2
Shark 3	Ocelot 2
Snake 8	Mouse 1
Serval 0	Gorilla 9
Panda 7	Cat 4

247

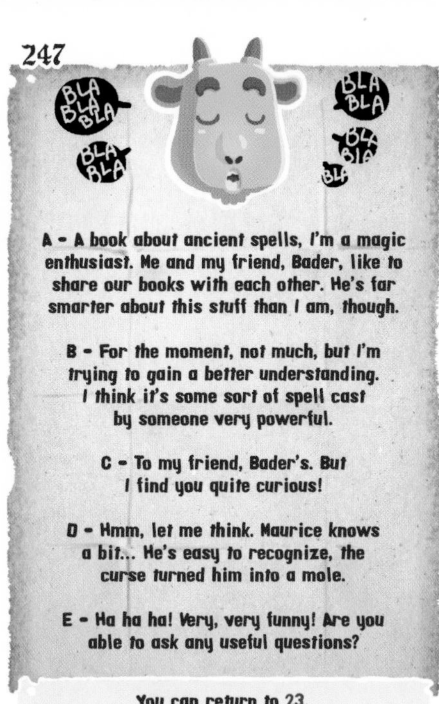

BLA BLA BLA
BLA BLA
BLA BLA
BLA BLA
BLA

A - A book about ancient spells, I'm a magic enthusiast. Me and my friend, Bader, like to share our books with each other. He's far smarter about this stuff than I am, though.

B - For the moment, not much, but I'm trying to gain a better understanding. I think it's some sort of spell cast by someone very powerful.

C - To my friend, Bader's. But I find you quite curious!

D - Hmm, let me think. Maurice knows a bit... He's easy to recognize, the curse turned him into a mole.

E - Ha ha ha! Very, very funny! Are you able to ask any useful questions?

You can return to 23.

248

Wanosh, the powerful sorcerer, guarded the Moose people and the city for many decades. He perished combatting invaders during the attack of lunar year 7487. In spite of that, he succeeded in preserving the sanctuary and the sacred stone: the ruby.

Legend says that shortly before his death, Wanosh made a pact with the stone gods. Whoever stole the sacred stone would trigger a terrible curse.

You can return to 160 or turn back to 16.

249

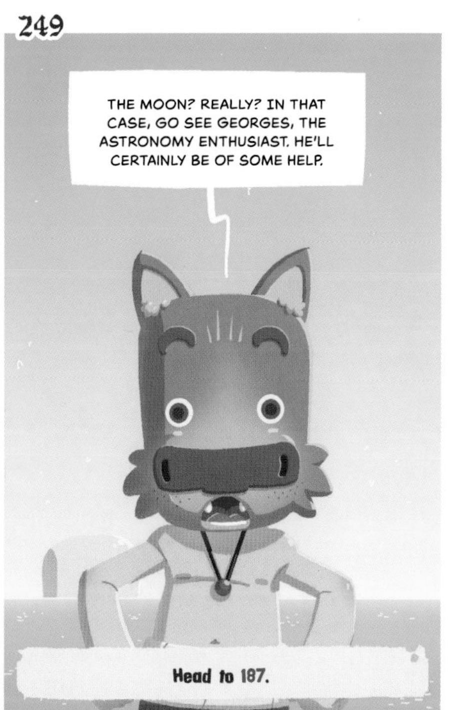

THE MOON? REALLY? IN THAT CASE, GO SEE GEORGES, THE ASTRONOMY ENTHUSIAST. HE'LL CERTAINLY BE OF SOME HELP.

Head to 187.

250

198

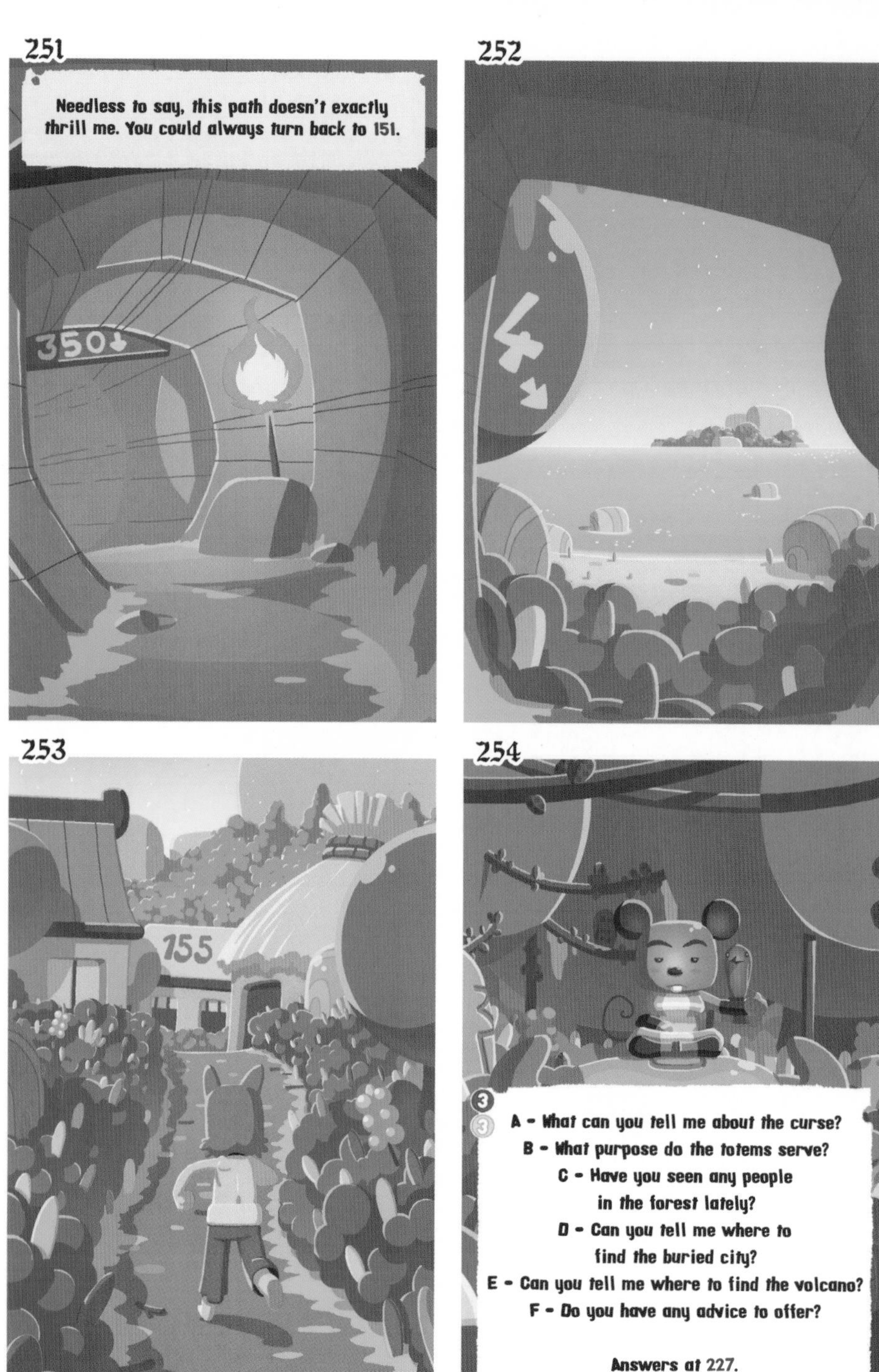
251
Needless to say, this path doesn't exactly thrill me. You could always turn back to 151.
350
252
4
253
155
254
3
3
A - What can you tell me about the curse?
B - What purpose do the totems serve?
C - Have you seen any people in the forest lately?
D - Can you tell me where to find the buried city?
E - Can you tell me where to find the volcano?
F - Do you have any advice to offer?
Answers at 227.

255

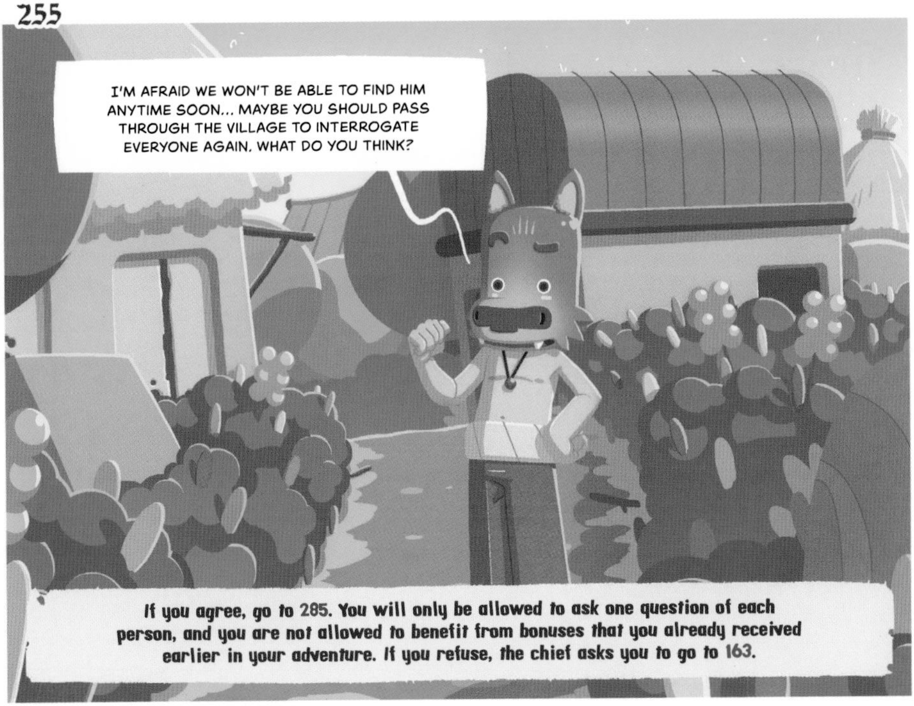

I'M AFRAID WE WON'T BE ABLE TO FIND HIM ANYTIME SOON... MAYBE YOU SHOULD PASS THROUGH THE VILLAGE TO INTERROGATE EVERYONE AGAIN. WHAT DO YOU THINK?

If you agree, go to 285. You will only be allowed to ask one question of each person, and you are not allowed to benefit from bonuses that you already received earlier in your adventure. If you refuse, the chief asks you to go to 163.

256

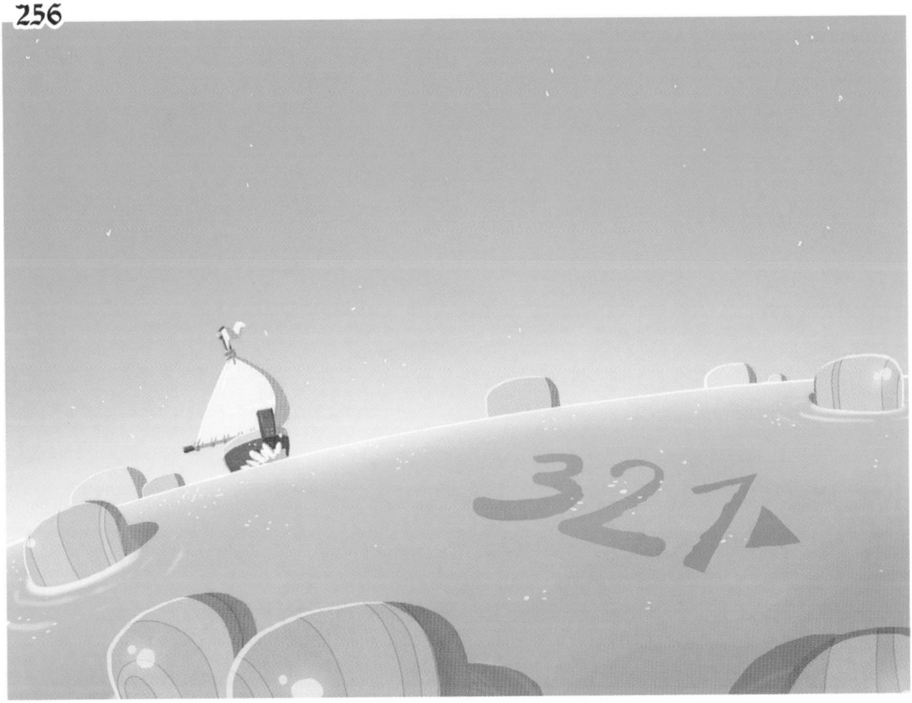

321

257

2
3

A - What are you doing here?
B - Who are you?
C - Were you here when the curse hit?
D - What do you do for work?
E - Do you know where this path leads?
F - Who can help me learn more about the curse?
G - How long have you lived in the village?
H - Do you know the person who transformed into a gazelle?

Answers at 215.

258

161

259

Unfortunately, I'm afraid you aren't welcome here. These pirates are less friendly than the ones in your crew and will be feeding you to the sharks shortly... You've lost, but you can restart your adventure on page 2.

260

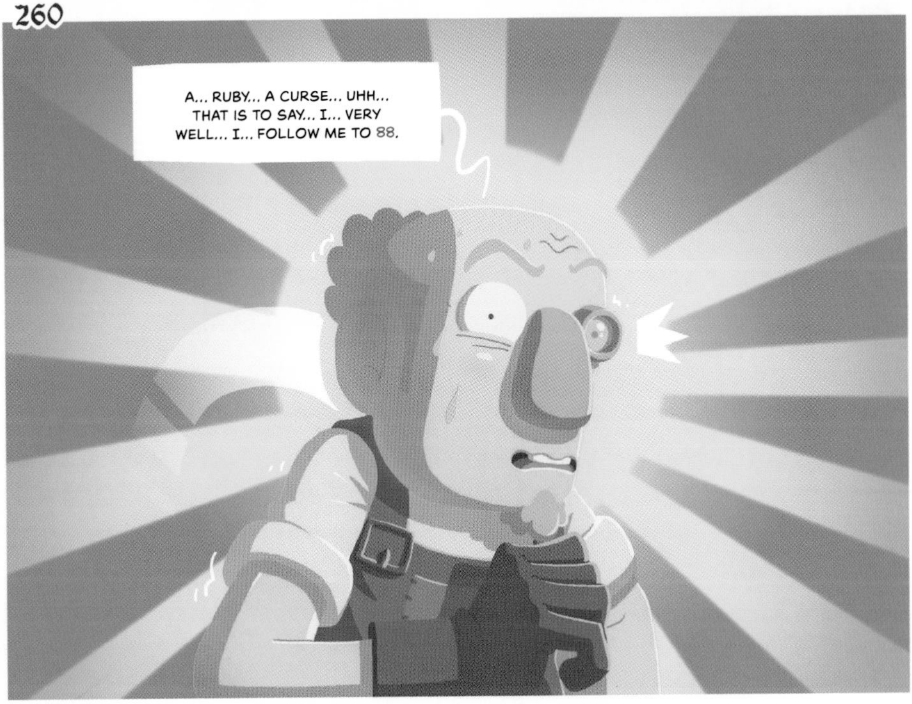

A... RUBY... A CURSE... UHH... THAT IS TO SAY... I... VERY WELL... I... FOLLOW ME TO 88.

261

329

262

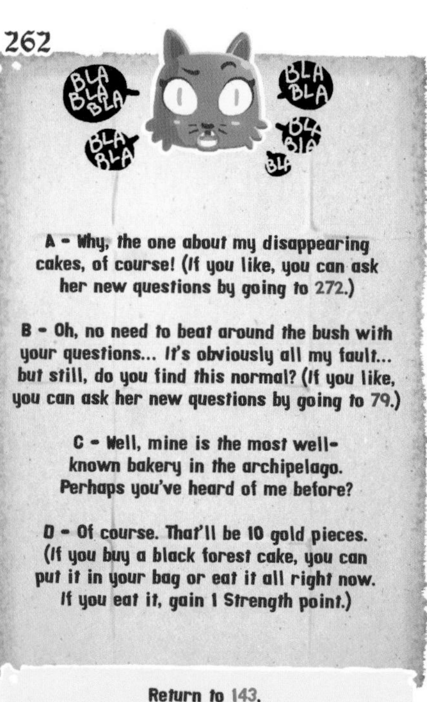
BLA BLA BLA
BLA BLA
BLA BLA
BLA BLA
BLA

A - Why, the one about my disappearing cakes, of course! (If you like, you can ask her new questions by going to 272.)

B - Oh, no need to beat around the bush with your questions... It's obviously all my fault... but still, do you find this normal? (If you like, you can ask her new questions by going to 79.)

C - Well, mine is the most well-known bakery in the archipelago. Perhaps you've heard of me before?

D - Of course. That'll be 10 gold pieces. (If you buy a black forest cake, you can put it in your bag or eat it all right now. If you eat it, gain 1 Strength point.)

Return to 143.

263

AND IT TOOK YOU ALL THIS TIME TO COME UP WITH THIS RIDICULOUS THEORY? GET OUT! I DON'T WANT TO SEE YOU AGAIN!

Your adventure ends here. You're all washed up, but you can restart your adventure on page 2.

264

336

265

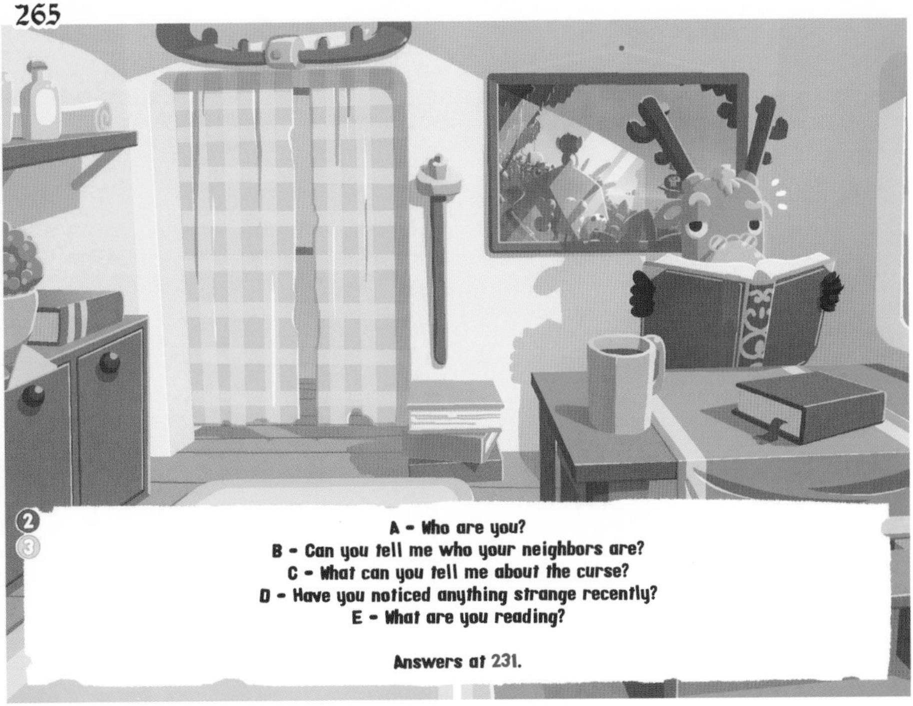

A - Who are you?
B - Can you tell me who your neighbors are?
C - What can you tell me about the curse?
D - Have you noticed anything strange recently?
E - What are you reading?

Answers at 231.

266

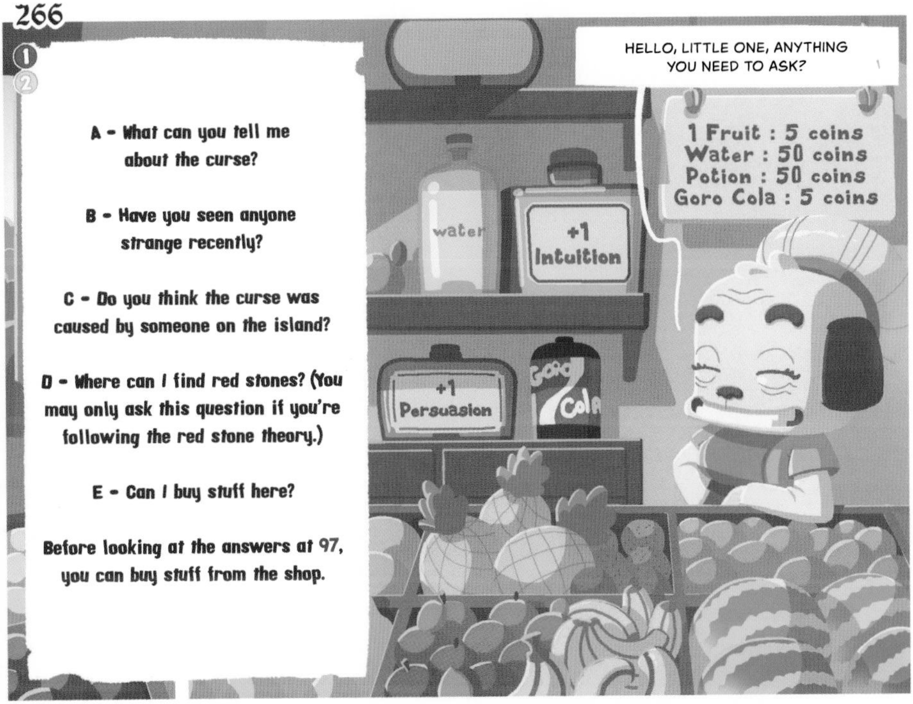

HELLO, LITTLE ONE, ANYTHING YOU NEED TO ASK?

1 Fruit : 5 coins
Water : 50 coins
Potion : 50 coins
Goro Cola : 5 coins

water

+1 Intuition

+1 Persuasion

Goro Cola

A - What can you tell me about the curse?

B - Have you seen anyone strange recently?

C - Do you think the curse was caused by someone on the island?

D - Where can I find red stones? (You may only ask this question if you're following the red stone theory.)

E - Can I buy stuff here?

Before looking at the answers at 97, you can buy stuff from the shop.

267

BLA BLA BLA
BLA BLA

BLA BLA

A - I don't have any formal occupation to speak of, but I am an expert on precious and semi-precious stones. Stones are my greatest passion.

B - That has been under our noses for a long time...

C - Everyone in the village has their own little theory. Some of them are crazy, but others make some sense. In my opinion, Bader, Georges and Gauthier have the most interesting ideas on the subject.

D - Hmm... Interesting. One can't find stones like these on this island. This red is typical of the mountains on neighboring islands.

E - Because nothing good ever comes from digging around and sticking our nose in things ... That's why.

F - I'm talking about Jenova Island. It's the island behind that of the Patikas.

You can return to 143.

268

A great shaman once said: "Respect the forest or it will play tricks on you." Cutting vines doesn't sound like something the forest appreciates. You seem to be caught in a trap. I imagine the forest will get over it and let you go in a few hours. In the meantime, blood is rushing to your head, and you lose – hang on (haha!) – 2 Intelligence points, 2 Intuition points, and 1 Strength point. You can now continue to 169.

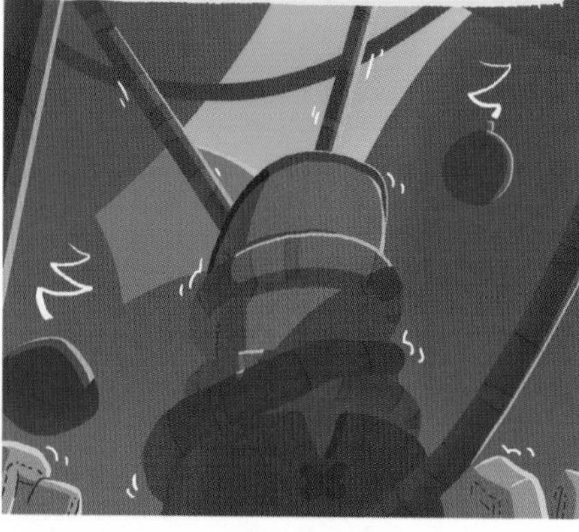

269

Clearly, you asked the wrong question. Return from whence you came.

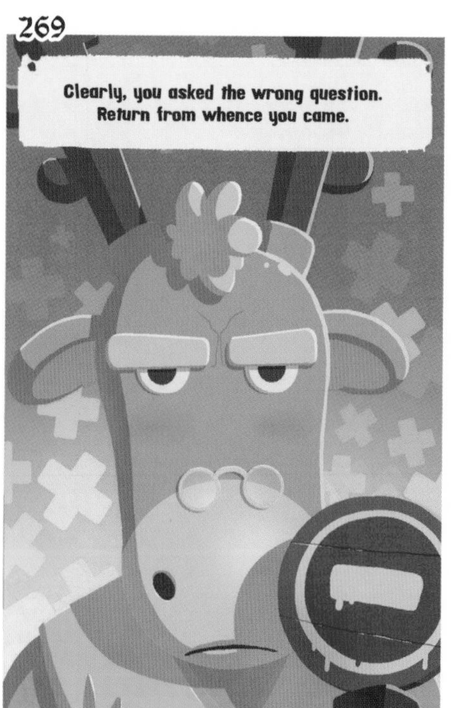

270

Are you sure about this? Perhaps it would be wiser to turn around and head back to Shukanet Island? If you wish to continue, go to 74. To turn back, go to 217.

271

NOW, NOW! OF COURSE, I COULD GIVE YOU THE ANSWER, BUT WOULD THAT HELP YOU? GO ON, GET OUTTA HERE! DO ME A FAVOR: RETURN WHERE YOU CAME FROM AND FINISH THIS ADVENTURE BY THE BOOK, PUN INTENDED!
VER
SCRIPT
blablablabla blablablabla et blablabla, et blablabla blablablabla bla bla bla and suddenly blabla! argh! bla n'a didn't see coming! blablabla bla . Cependant : bla bla, ha-ha ! Evan loves Kristena, blabla blablabla

272

A - What are you even talking about? I'm here to investigate the curse cast upon this village.

B - Tell me more. When did you notice the cakes had been stolen?

C - What kind of cakes were stolen?

D - Where do you think the thief went?

E - *Don't* you think there might be more *important* things to worry about than some stolen cakes? Honestly.

F - *Is* this the first time your cakes have been stolen?

Answers at 106.

273

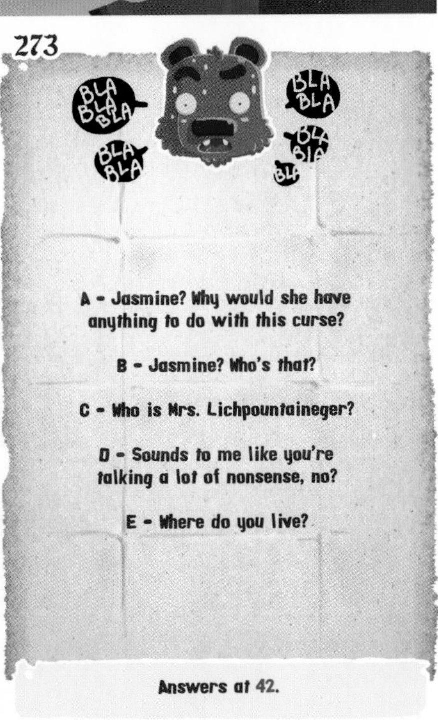
BLA BLA BLA
BLA BLA
BLA BLA
BLA BLA
BLA

A - Jasmine? Why would she have anything to do with this curse?

B - Jasmine? Who's that?

C - Who is Mrs. Lichpountaineger?

D - Sounds to me like you're talking a lot of nonsense, no?

E - Where do you live?

Answers at 42.

274

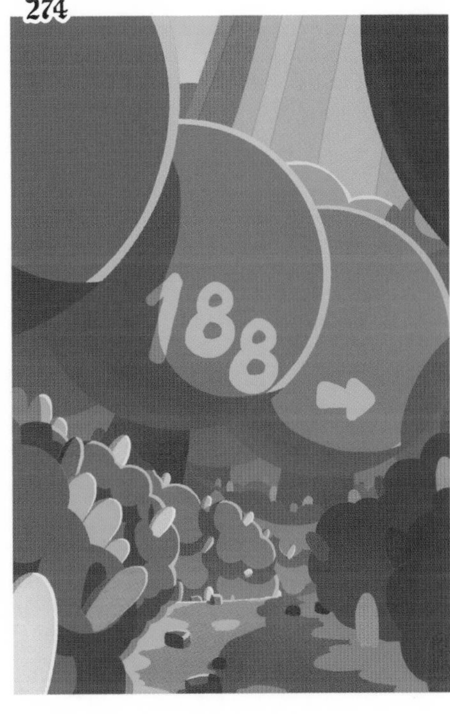
188

275

ENJOY THE PRIVILEGES OF BEING SECOND IN COMMAND, CABIN BOY! GO TO PAGE 3.

This well earned break causes you to gain 1 Strength point.

276

92

277

250

261

278

PIRATE, YOU HAVE FAILED TO LIVE UP TO YOUR REPUTATION. YOU WRONGLY ACCUSED AN INNCOCENT PARTY, WHO, BY THE WAY, WAS TRAUMATIZED BY YOUR INTERROGATION. IN SPITE OF THAT, IT SEEMS YOU WERE ABLE TO SOLVE THE MYSTERY OF THE DISAPPEARING CAKES, SO I WILL ALLOW YOU TO CONTINUE YOUR INVESTIGATION. YOU CAN RETURN TO THE VILLAGE TO CONTINUE INTERROGATING, BUT YOU MAY ONLY ASK EACH PERSON ONE QUESTION.
You now have a yellow card, which weighs nothing in your bag. Oh, I almost forgot! Before heading to 285, subtract 2 Intuition points to better reflect your brilliant analytical mind...

279

WATCH YOUR HEAD!

153

280

ELLIOT ISN'T VERY BIG, HAS A SMALL GOATEE, A PURSE STRAPPED TO HIS BELT AND AN EXPERT MAGNIFYING GLASS. YOU'LL ONLY BE ABLE TO SPEAK WITH HIM IF YOU UNDERSTAND ROMAN NUMERALS. HERE'S A LITTLE PRIMER BEHIND ME, IF IT'LL HELP YOU.

NOW, GET BACK TO 210. YOU MIGHT BE ABLE TO FIND HIM THERE.

C=100 III=3
IX=9 L=50
CL=150
XX=20

281

319
21

282

Clearly, that was the wrong question.
Return whence you came.

283

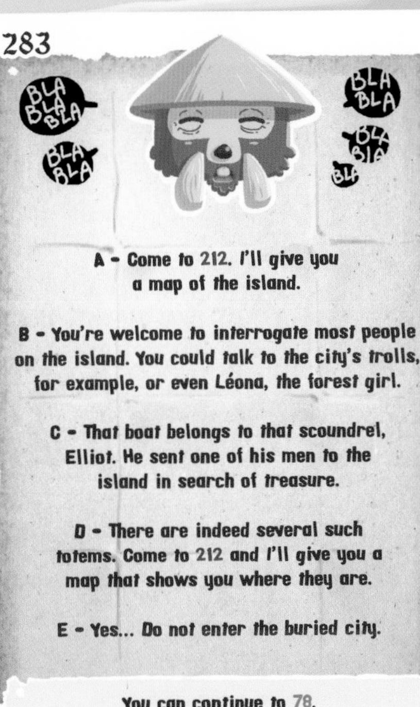

BLA BLA BLA
BLA BLA
BLA BLA

A - Come to 212. I'll give you a map of the island.

B - You're welcome to interrogate most people on the island. You could talk to the city's trolls, for example, or even Léona, the forest girl.

C - That boat belongs to that scoundrel, Elliot. He sent one of his men to the island in search of treasure.

D - There are indeed several such totems. Come to 212 and I'll give you a map that shows you where they are.

E - Yes... Do not enter the buried city.

You can continue to 78.

284

TALES OF MEN
19579 63 278
145

285

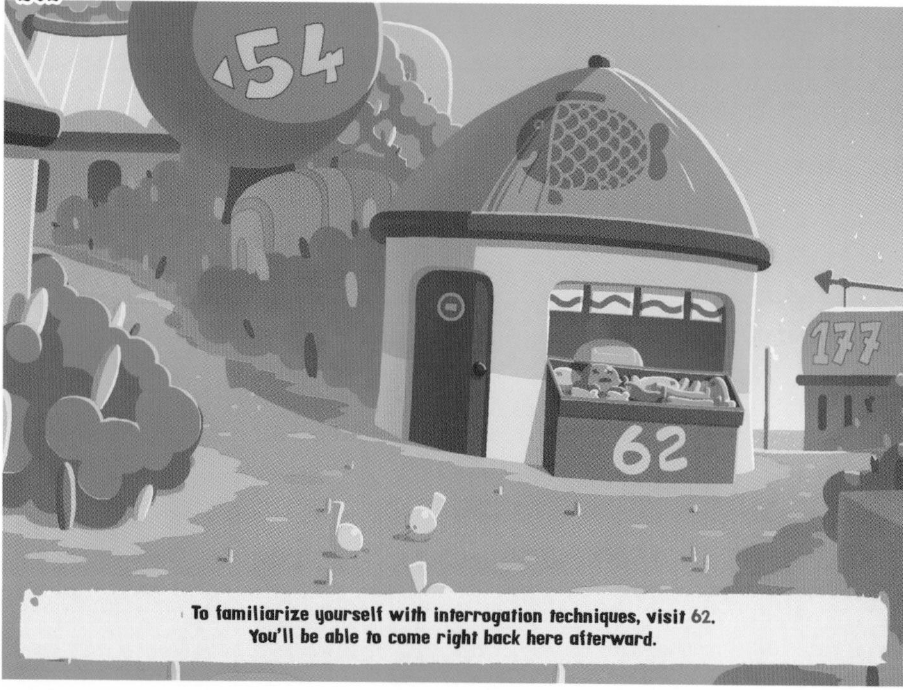

To familiarize yourself with interrogation techniques, visit 62.
You'll be able to come right back here afterward.

286

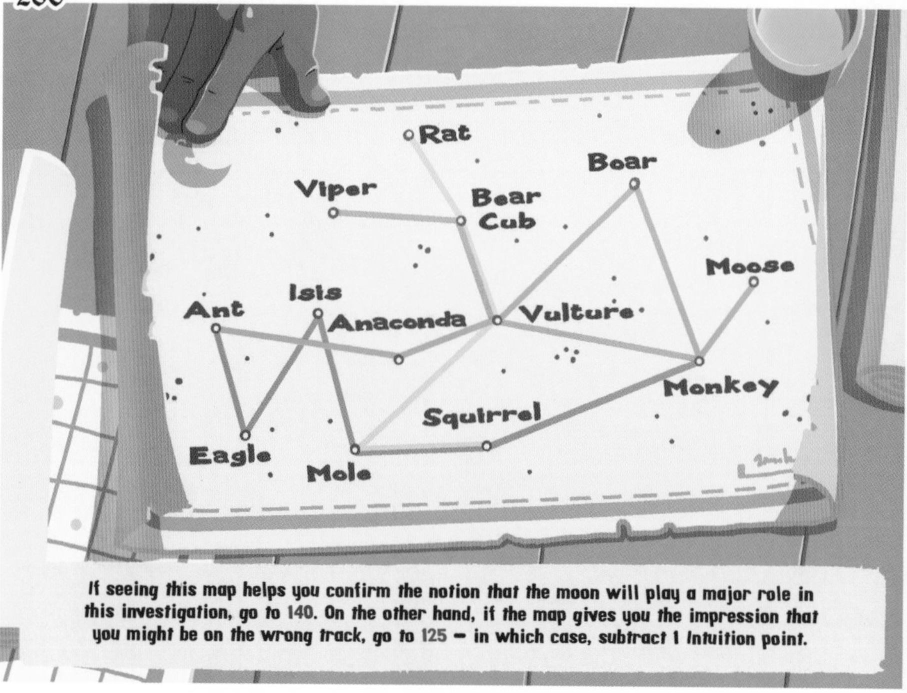

If seeing this map helps you confirm the notion that the moon will play a major role in this investigation, go to 140. On the other hand, if the map gives you the impression that you might be on the wrong track, go to 125 – in which case, subtract 1 Intuition point.

287

HMM! MAYBE YOU SHOULD TAKE ANOTHER TOUR AROUND THE VILLAGE, WHAT DO YOU THINK? DOING SO WOULD ALLOW YOU TO OBTAIN ADDITIONAL INFORMATION TO SECURE YOUR THEORY.
OR IT WILL SHOW YOU HOW BAD OF AN INVESTIGATOR YOU ARE.
Return to the village entrance at 285 and interrogate the villagers again. Maybe you'll have better luck this time.

288

43

289

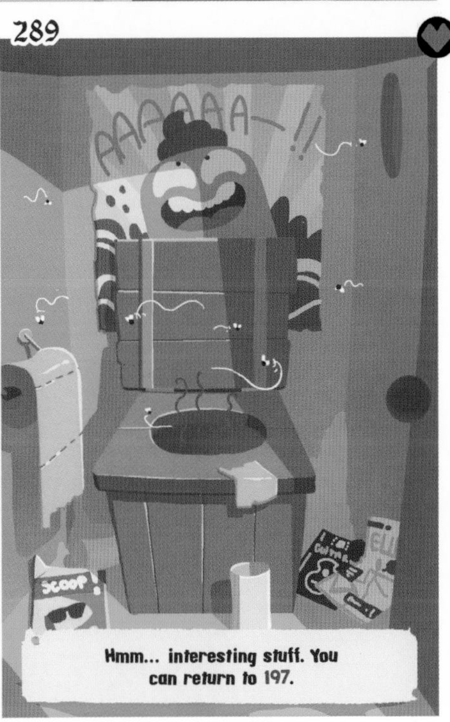
AAAAAA—!!
SCOOP!
Hmm... interesting stuff. You can return to 197.

290

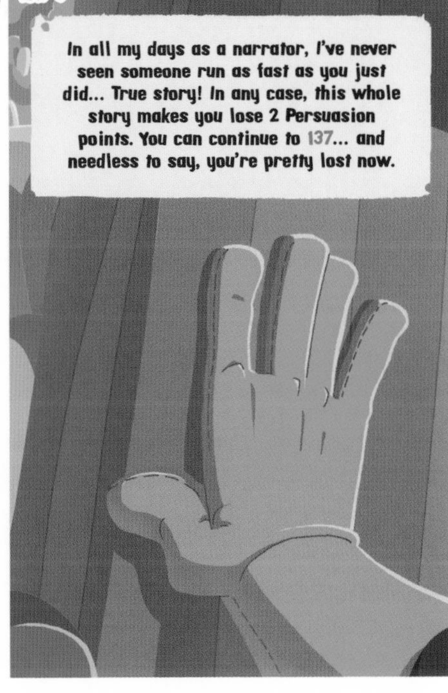
In all my days as a narrator, I've never seen someone run as fast as you just did... True story! In any case, this whole story makes you lose 2 Persuasion points. You can continue to 137... and needless to say, you're pretty lost now.

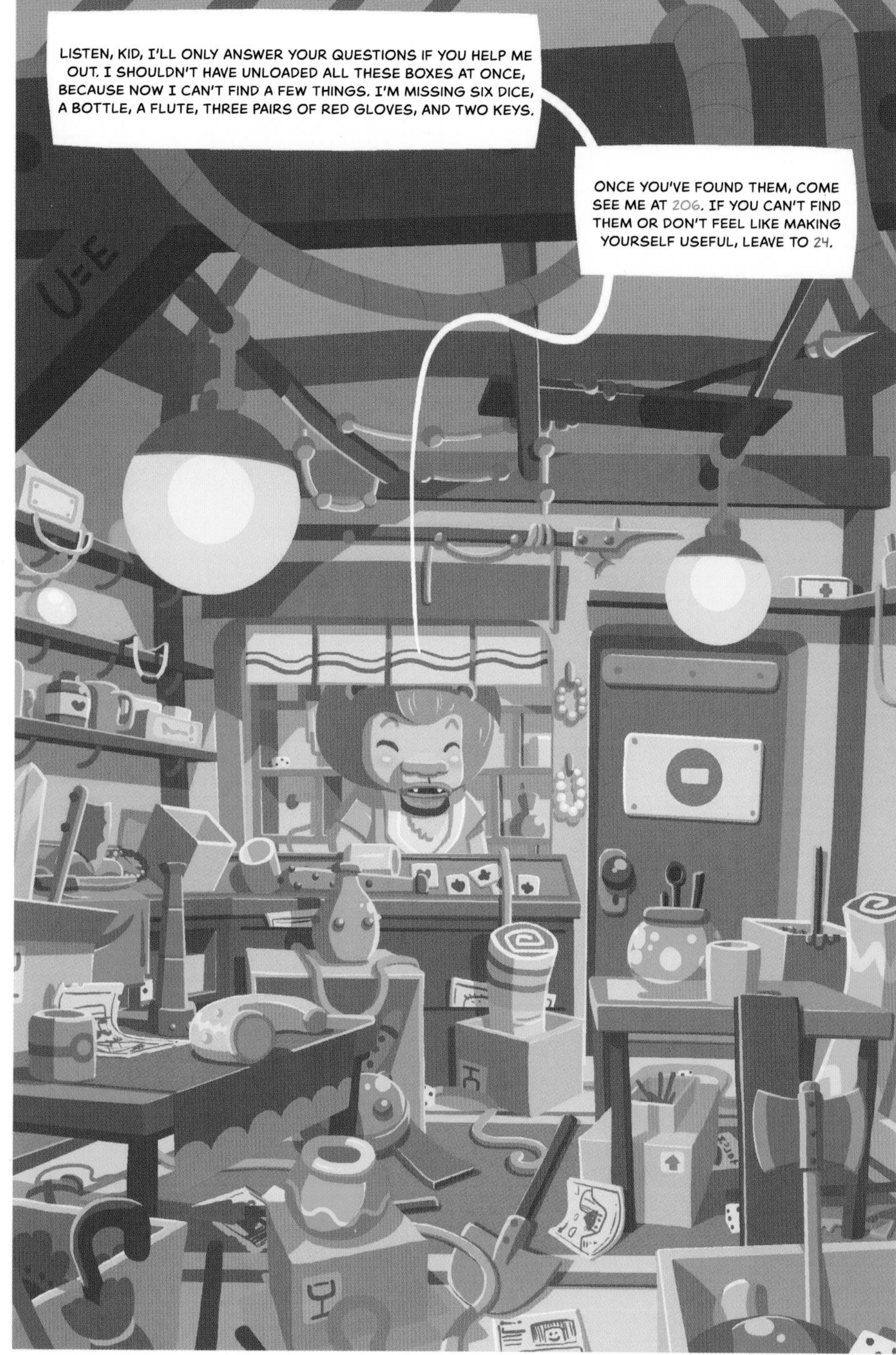
LISTEN, KID, I'LL ONLY ANSWER YOUR QUESTIONS IF YOU HELP ME OUT. I SHOULDN'T HAVE UNLOADED ALL THESE BOXES AT ONCE, BECAUSE NOW I CAN'T FIND A FEW THINGS. I'M MISSING SIX DICE, A BOTTLE, A FLUTE, THREE PAIRS OF RED GLOVES, AND TWO KEYS.
ONCE YOU'VE FOUND THEM, COME SEE ME AT 206. IF YOU CAN'T FIND THEM OR DON'T FEEL LIKE MAKING YOURSELF USEFUL, LEAVE TO 24.
U=E

292

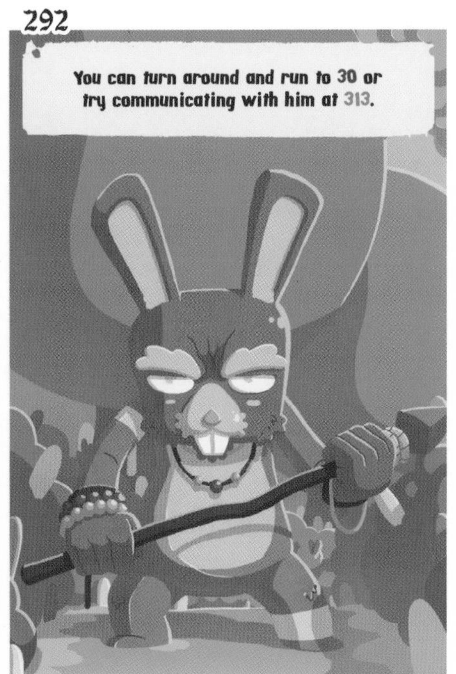
You can turn around and run to 30 or try communicating with him at 313.

293

294

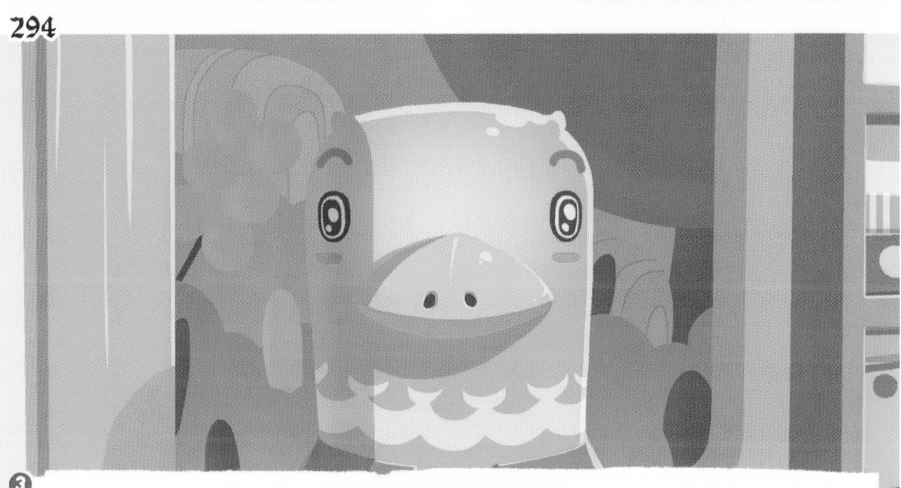
A - Do you live alone here?
B - Can you tell me more about Jasmine?
C - Can you tell me more about Mr. Gazelle?
D - Can you tell me where I can find a geologist?
E - Did you see anything peculiar shortly before or after the curse hit the village?
F - What's your neighbor's name?
Answers at 300.

295
I'M BEGINNING TO WONDER IF YOU'VE LOST YOUR MIND, YOU POOR THING.
Something tells me he's not quite convinced by your brilliant mind and investigative talents. You can restart on page 2.

296
FOR GOODNESS' SAKE! CAN I PLEASE JUST WRITE IN SILENCE FOR ONE DAY? THESE STONES COME FROM JENOVA. JE-NO-VA... GOT IT?
Some incredible Intuition right there! You might be on the right track after all. Gain 1 intuition point. Now follow Esteban to 135.

297
A BOAT? REALLY? IF YOU SAY SO. I KNOW SOMEONE WHO MIGHT BE ABLE TO HELP. FOLLOW ME TO 14.

298
210

299

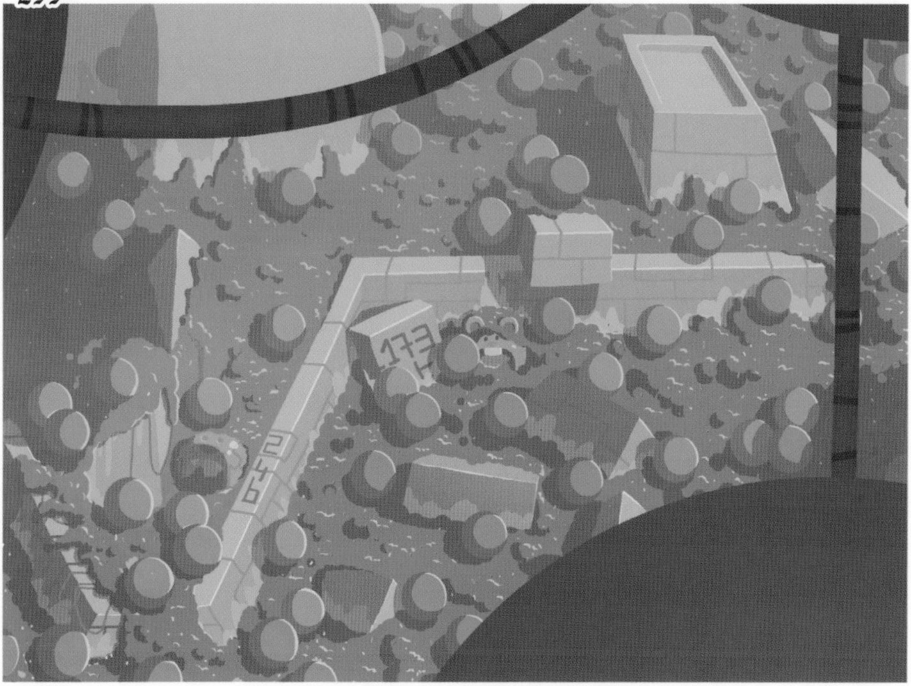

300

A - OH YES, I'VE LIVED ALONE HERE FOR YEARS, BUT I HAVE A MAGNIFICENT VIEW AND MANY FRIENDS IN THE VILLAGE, SO I NEVER FEEL ISOLATED, YOU KNOW?

B - I SAW THAT ONE COMING! YOU KNOW ABOUT HER SECRET, TOO? I CAN'T REALLY DIVULGE ANYTHING, BUT ONE THING'S FOR SURE, SHE'S A SECRETIVE ONE, THAT GIRL.

C - OF COURSE, I CAN TELL YOU THAT HE'S NOT THE BACHELOR HE MAKES HIMSELF OUT TO BE... IF YOU GET MY DRIFT.

D - MAURICE IS PASSIONATE ABOUT STONES, HE HANGS AROUND ROCKS AND SUCH A LOT. THERE'S A LITTLE PASSAGE TO THE RIGHT OF HIS HOUSE THAT GOES DOWN TO THE SEA. GO TO 29 WHEN YOU'RE DONE ASKING ME QUESTIONS.

E - APART FROM A SHIP WITH THREE MASTS THAT DROPPED ANCHOR CLOSER TO THE NEIGHBORING ISLAND, NO.

F - GEORGES, UNDER HIS HARD RHINOCEROS EXTERIOR, HE'S QUITE A CHARMING NEIGHBOR. TELL HIM I SAY HI.

You can return to 119.

301

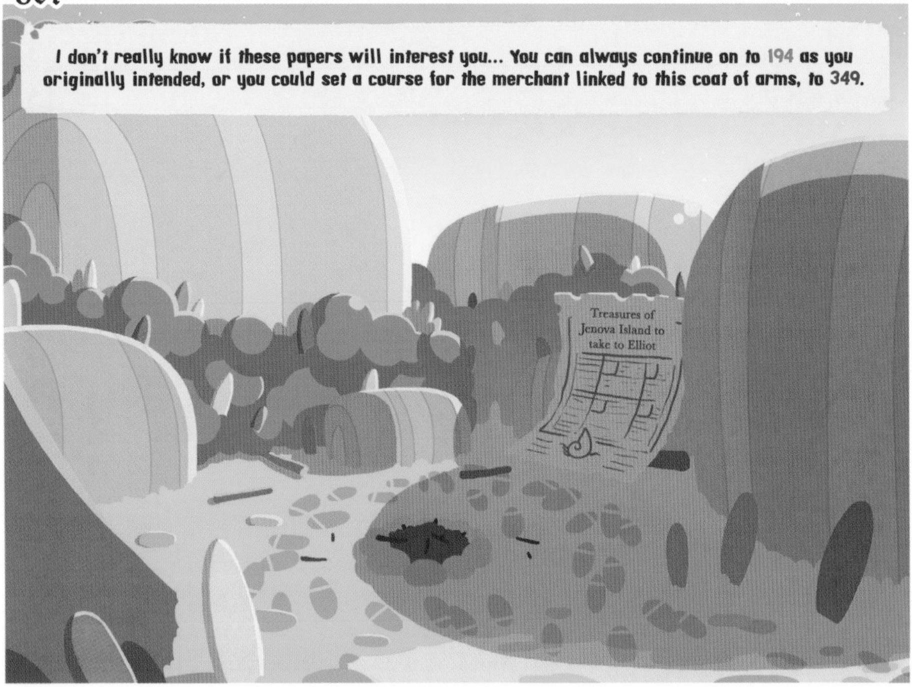

I don't really know if these papers will interest you... You can always continue on to 194 as you originally intended, or you could set a course for the merchant linked to this coat of arms, to 349.

302

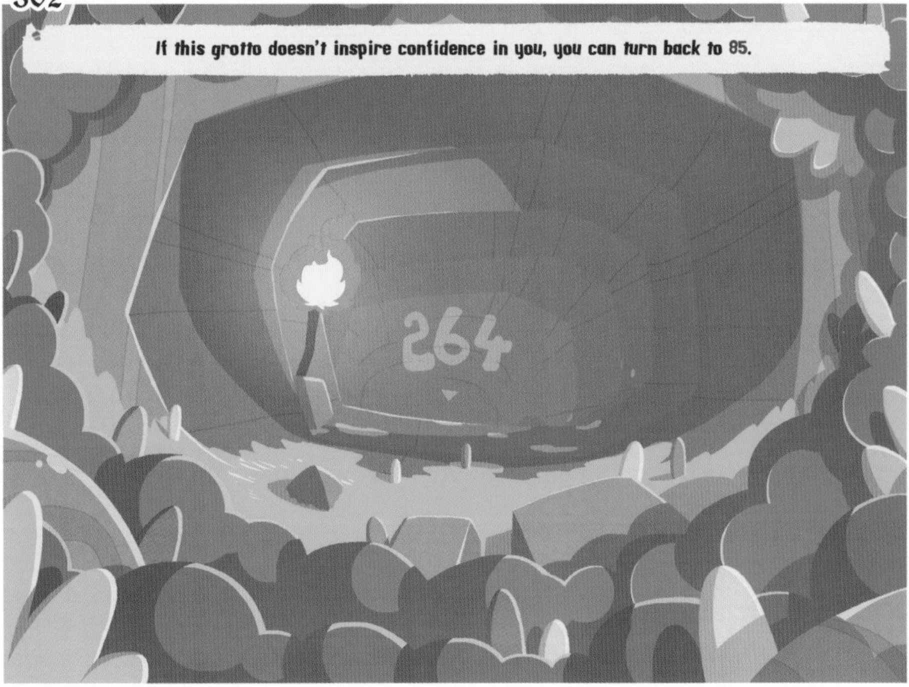

If this grotto doesn't inspire confidence in you, you can turn back to 85.

303

If you have more than 10 Intuition, you can enter the jungle by following the path at 327. You can also turn back to 195.

304

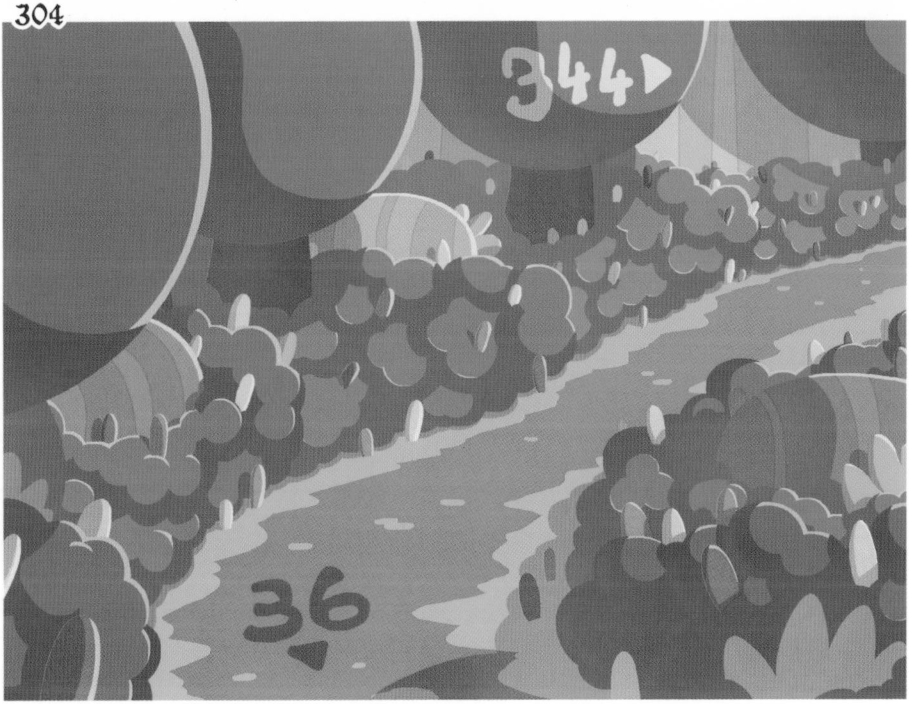

305

If you have more than 10 Persuasion, you command the individual to stop at 89 and return his clothes. Otherwise, you can go to 51.

306

HEY WAIT HAVE YOU BOUGHT THESE BOOKS!?

AT LEAST BUY THE FIRST TWO PIRATES BOOKS! WAIT, YOU HAVE THEM? WHAT ABOUT THE CRUSOE CREW?

LILLY VAN HELSING
CANADA
CRUSOE CREW

307

I SEE... SO, THESE WRETCHED RED STONES CAUSED THIS CURSE? DO YOU KNOW WHAT WE NEED TO DO TO REVERSE IT?

If you think that you need to clean the beach and toss the stones in the water, go to 34. If you believe that you need to go to the source of the stones, go to 325. If you figure there's nothing to be done, go to 140.

308

Another totem... Take a good look, maybe it will answer one of your many questions.

16→

309

310

311

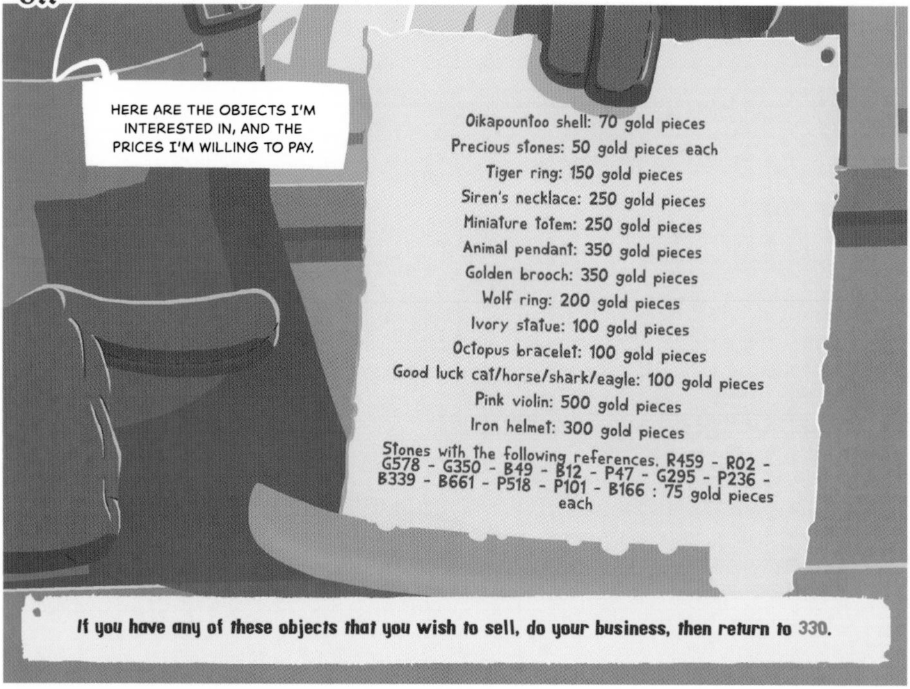

HERE ARE THE OBJECTS I'M INTERESTED IN, AND THE PRICES I'M WILLING TO PAY.

Oikapountoo shell: 70 gold pieces
Precious stones: 50 gold pieces each
Tiger ring: 150 gold pieces
Siren's necklace: 250 gold pieces
Miniature totem: 250 gold pieces
Animal pendant: 350 gold pieces
Golden brooch: 350 gold pieces
Wolf ring: 200 gold pieces
Ivory statue: 100 gold pieces
Octopus bracelet: 100 gold pieces
Good luck cat/horse/shark/eagle: 100 gold pieces
Pink violin: 500 gold pieces
Iron helmet: 300 gold pieces
Stones with the following references. R459 - R02 - G578 - G350 - B49 - B12 - P47 - G295 - P236 - B339 - B661 - P518 - P101 - B166 : 75 gold pieces each

If you have any of these objects that you wish to sell, do your business, then return to 330.

312

... THIS CAN'T GO ON, I CAN'T PLAY FLUTE WITH THESE PAWS ANYMORE!

YES, AND IN ADDITION TO THE APPEARANCE, THERE ARE CERTAIN ANIMAL BEHAVIORS THAT COME WITH... I NEEDN'T DESCRIBE THE STATE OF THE WALLS IN MY HOUSE... UGH.

TAKE A CHAIR AT 222.

313

Reflect carefully on the question you wish to ask... your adventure depends on it! Go to 38 for your answer.

A - Who are you?
B - Where is the red and white boat?
C - Where are the mines?
D - What do you know about the curse?
E - Can you help me find my way?

314

315

A - Go To 200

B - Go To 244

C - Go To 263

D - Go To 348

E - Go To 295

F - Go To 58

G - Go To 265

H - Go To 295

I - Go To 244

J - Go To 192

K - Go To 263

L - Go To 192

M - Go To 118

N - Go To 348

316

BLA BLA

BLA BLA
BLA

A - As it happens... These are books about the Moose, my ancestors. I... I think they're linked to this somehow.

B - I've been asking myself if it has anything to do with the fact that I'm the only one in the village who is truly native to this atoll.

C - My family were the first to have settled on this island, centuries ago.

D - Because I'm worried that they'll judge me, or that they'll think it's my fault. Simple as that.

E - Because I was pretty sure you thought this was somehow my fault.

Go to 55.

317

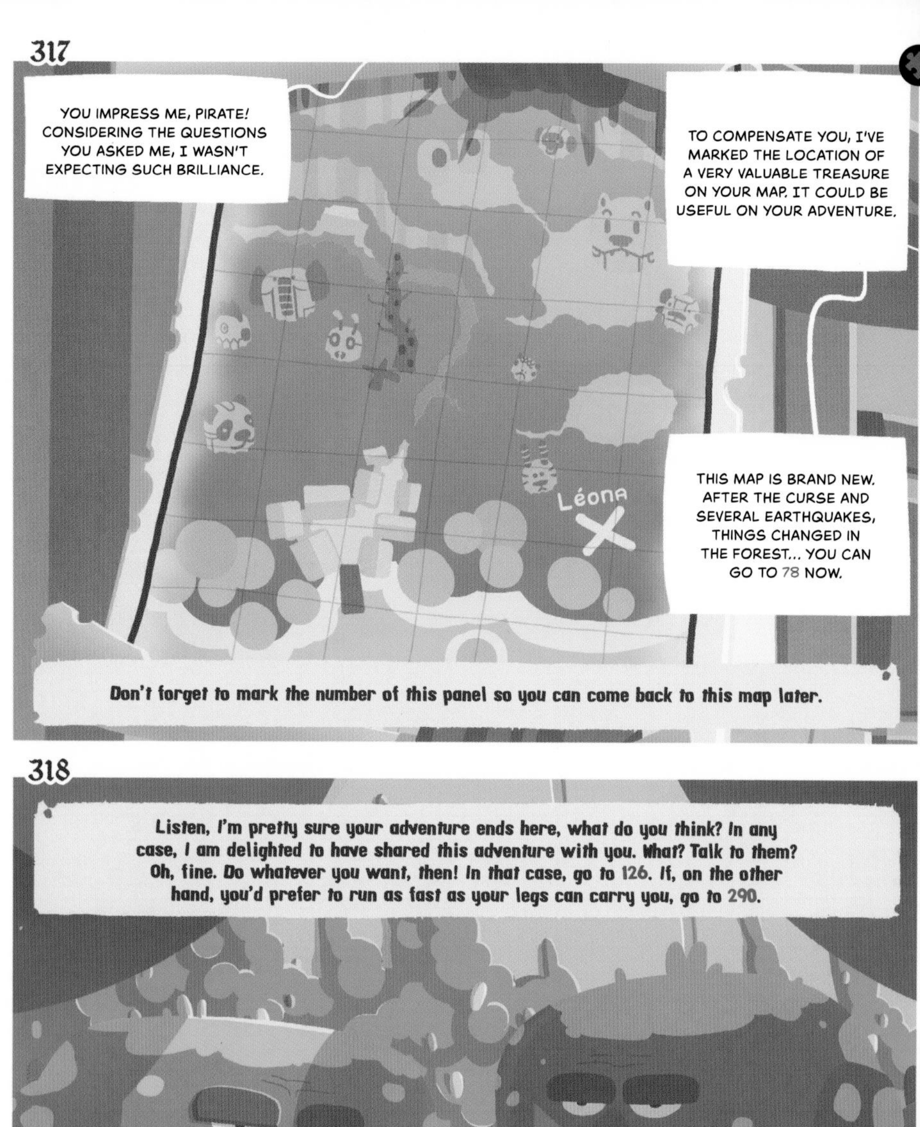
YOU IMPRESS ME, PIRATE! CONSIDERING THE QUESTIONS YOU ASKED ME, I WASN'T EXPECTING SUCH BRILLIANCE.
TO COMPENSATE YOU, I'VE MARKED THE LOCATION OF A VERY VALUABLE TREASURE ON YOUR MAP. IT COULD BE USEFUL ON YOUR ADVENTURE.
Léona
THIS MAP IS BRAND NEW. AFTER THE CURSE AND SEVERAL EARTHQUAKES, THINGS CHANGED IN THE FOREST... YOU CAN GO TO 78 NOW.
Don't forget to mark the number of this panel so you can come back to this map later.

318

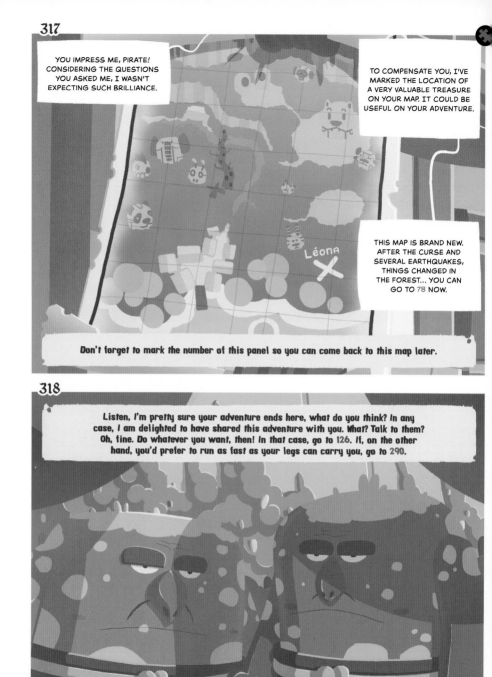

Listen, I'm pretty sure your adventure ends here, what do you think? In any case, I am delighted to have shared this adventure with you. What? Talk to them? Oh, fine. Do whatever you want, then! In that case, go to 126. If, on the other hand, you'd prefer to run as fast as your legs can carry you, go to 290.

319

36

320

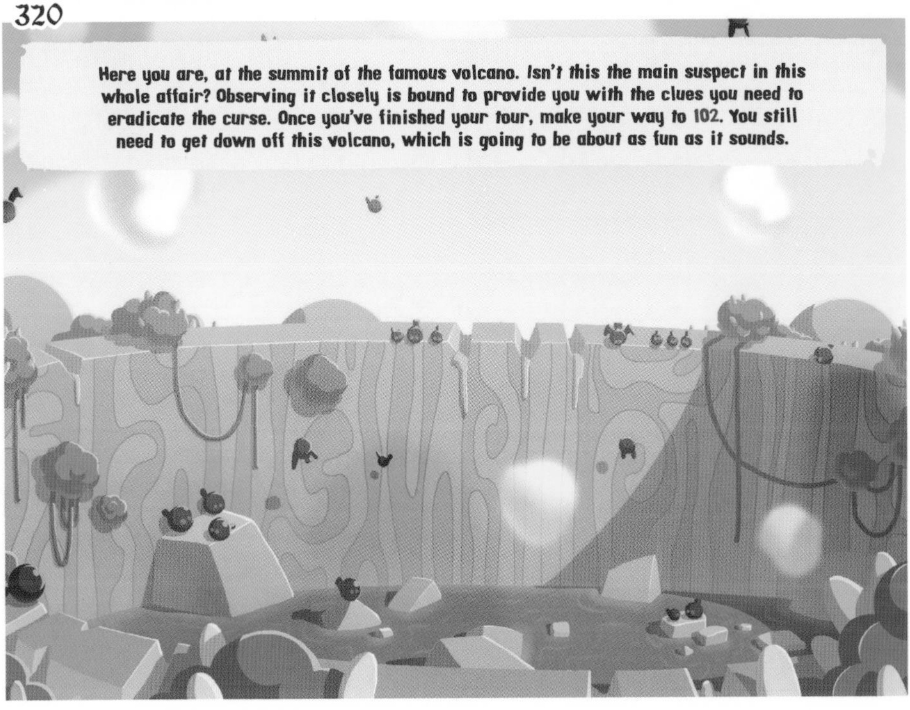

Here you are, at the summit of the famous volcano. *Isn't* this the main suspect in this whole affair? Observing it closely is bound to provide you with the clues you need to eradicate the curse. Once you've finished your tour, make your way to 102. You still need to get down off this volcano, which is going to be about as fun as it sounds.

321

After several days of drifting, your tummy starts to rumble. If you have any fishing equipment (harpoon, fishing rod, or hook), or if you have something to eat in your bag, everything is fine. If not, you lose 1 point from each of your Characteristics. You continue to 258.

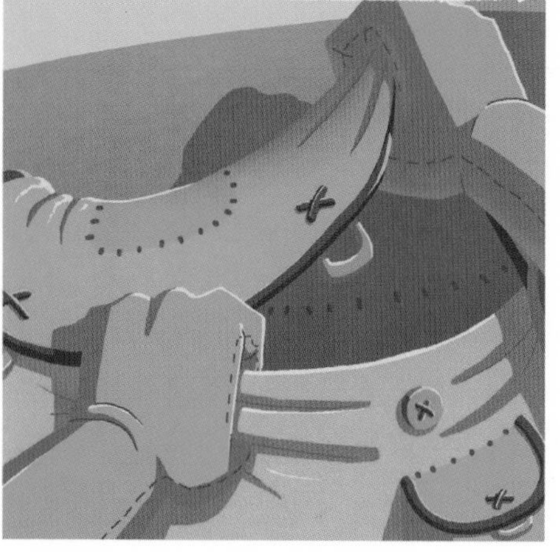

322

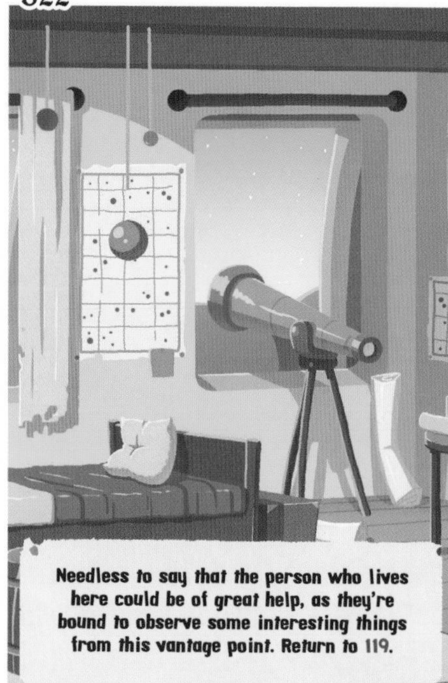
Needless to say that the person who lives here could be of great help, as they're bound to observe some interesting things from this vantage point. Return to 119.

323

ELLIOT? YES! TAKE THE FIRST RIGHT, AND THE SECOND. THEN, TAKE THE FOURTH LEFT. KEEP GOING STRAIGHT... STRAIGHT... STRAIGHT... AND TURN RIGHT AGAIN. YOU'LL ARRIVE AT A FORK. TAKE THE SMALLEST ROUTE ON YOUR LEFT, AND THAT'LL BRING YOU TO 225.

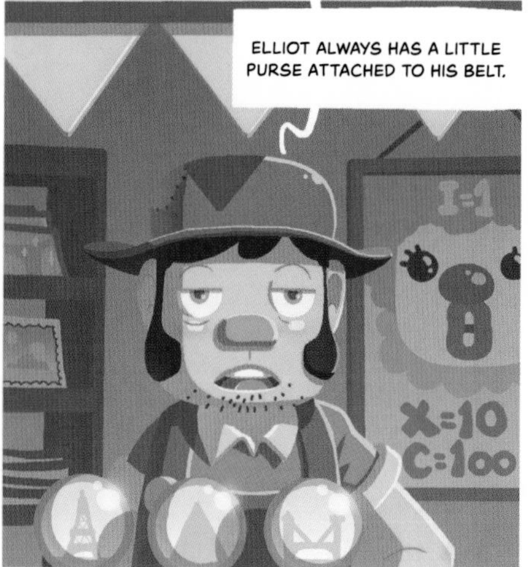
ELLIOT ALWAYS HAS A LITTLE PURSE ATTACHED TO HIS BELT.
I=1
X=10
C=100

324

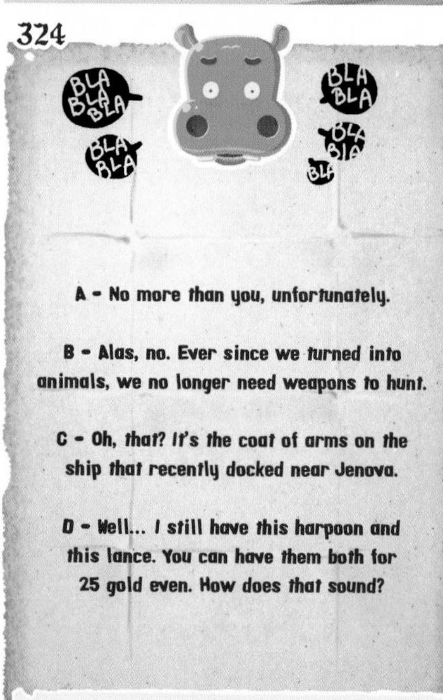
BLA BLA BLA
BLA BLA
BLA BLA
BLA BLA
BLA
A - No more than you, unfortunately.
B - Alas, no. Ever since we turned into animals, we no longer need weapons to hunt.
C - Oh, that? It's the coat of arms on the ship that recently docked near Jenova.
D - Well... I still have this harpoon and this lance. You can have them both for 25 gold even. How does that sound?

You can return to 240.

325

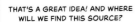

THAT'S A GREAT IDEA! AND WHERE WILL WE FIND THIS SOURCE?

If you think you need to go to Jenova Island to find it, go to 135. If you think Maurice can help you, go to 296. If you think Shuky can help, go to 271. If you have no idea whatsoever, go to 287.

326

107

327

101

This strange sculpture draws your attention. Overflowing with creativity, you decide to name it "strange sculpture". Note this name and continue along your route. Or you can turn back to 303.

328

24

329

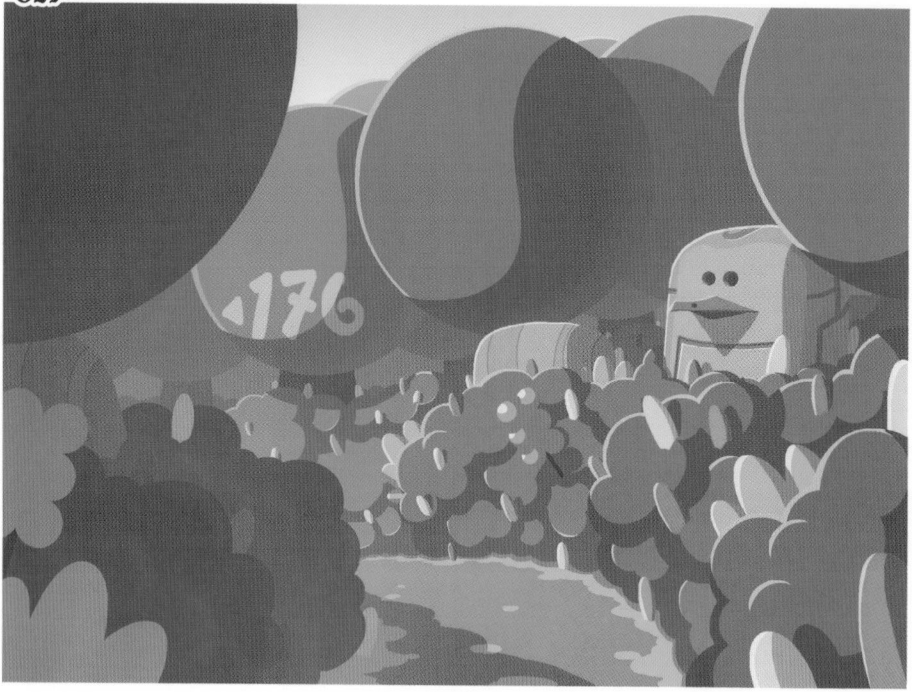

176

330

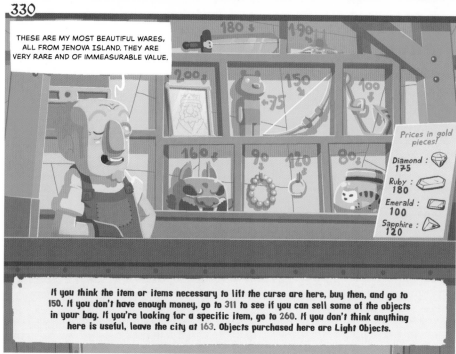

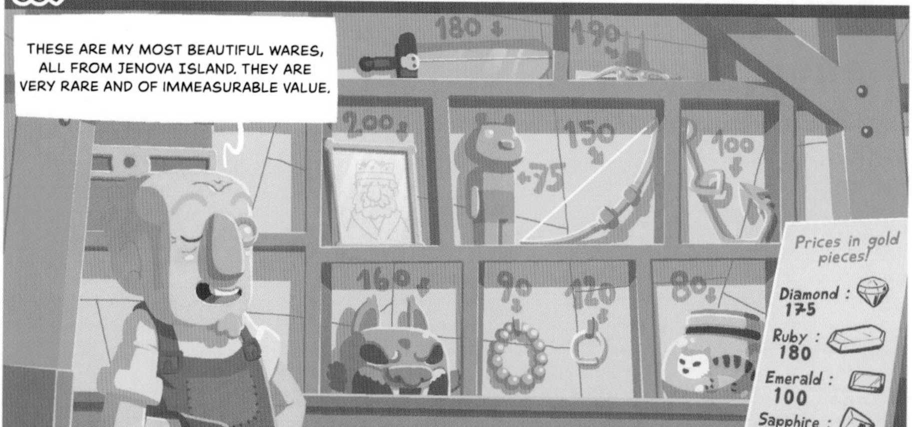

THESE ARE MY MOST BEAUTIFUL WARES, ALL FROM JENOVA ISLAND. THEY ARE VERY RARE AND OF IMMEASURABLE VALUE.

Prices in gold pieces!

Diamond : 175

Ruby : 180

Emerald : 100

Sapphire : 120

If you think the item or items necessary to lift the curse are here, buy then, and go to 150. If you don't have enough money, go to 311 to see if you can sell some of the objects in your bag. If you're looking for a specific item, go to 260. If you don't think anything here is useful, leave the city at 163. Objects purchased here are Light Objects.

331

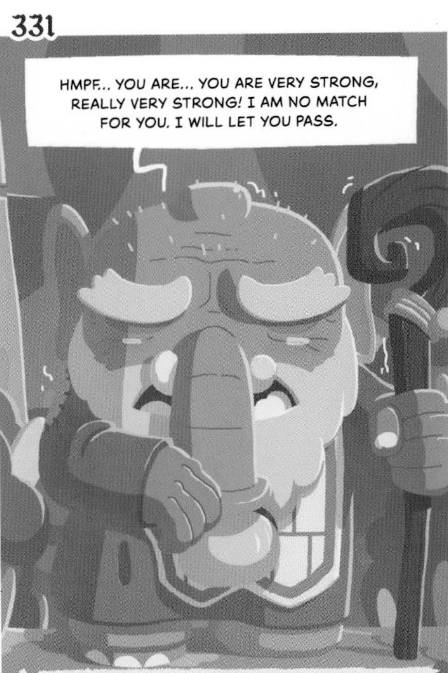
HMPF... YOU ARE... YOU ARE VERY STRONG, REALLY VERY STRONG! I AM NO MATCH FOR YOU. I WILL LET YOU PASS.
Pretty easy, no? Continue to 156.

332

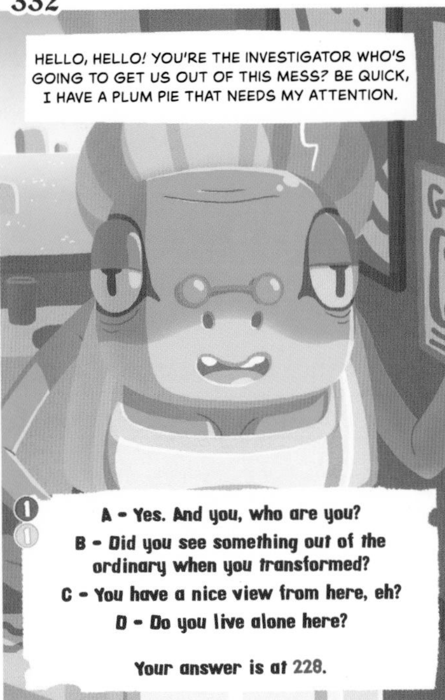
HELLO, HELLO! YOU'RE THE INVESTIGATOR WHO'S GOING TO GET US OUT OF THIS MESS? BE QUICK, I HAVE A PLUM PIE THAT NEEDS MY ATTENTION.
A - Yes. And you, who are you?
B - Did you see something out of the ordinary when you transformed?
C - You have a nice view from here, eh?
D - Do you live alone here?
Your answer is at 228.

333

The trick to obtaining the perfect blend of flavors is preparing each ingredient separately. Before cooking: peel the apple, remove the stone from the peach, remove the snail's antennae (this is the tough part), pick out the strawberry seeds, and remove the garlic peels.

When selecting a snail, choose one with a large shell. This will lend a crunchiness to your jam, which will help set your product apart.

?
Who else is hungry? You can return to 160 or go to 16.

334

73

335

YOU ARE DECIDEDLY THE WORST INVESTIGATOR THAT I HAVE EVER SEEN! WE NO LONGER NEED YOUR SERVICES. YOU CAN GO TO 163.

336

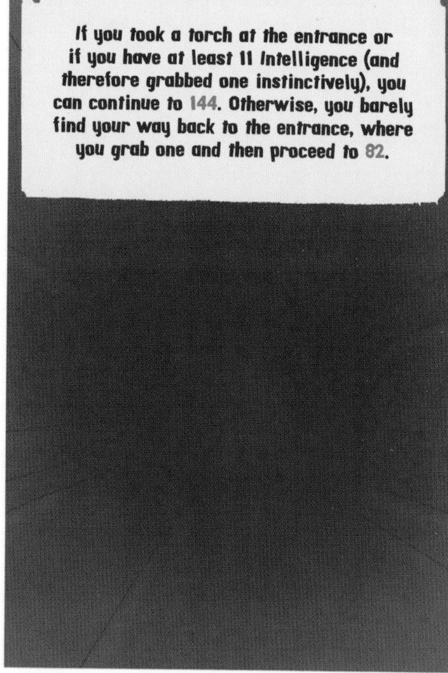
If you took a torch at the entrance or if you have at least 11 Intelligence (and therefore grabbed one instinctively), you can continue to 144. Otherwise, you barely find your way back to the entrance, where you grab one and then proceed to 82.

337

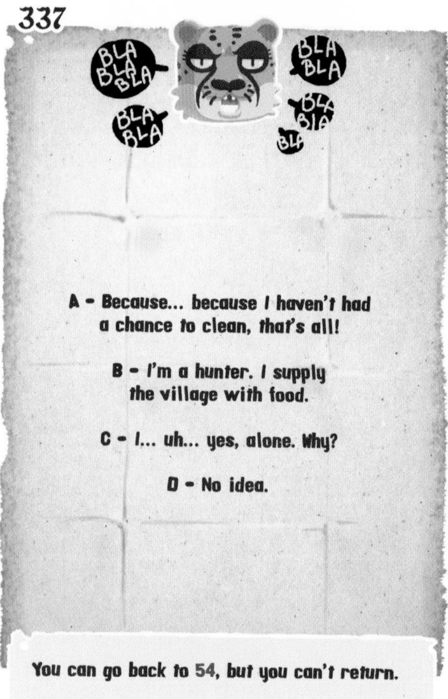
BLA BLA BLA
BLA BLA
BLA BLA
BLA BLA
BLA
A - Because... because I haven't had a chance to clean, that's all!
B - I'm a hunter. I supply the village with food.
C - I... uh... yes, alone. Why?
D - No idea.
You can go back to 54, but you can't return.

338

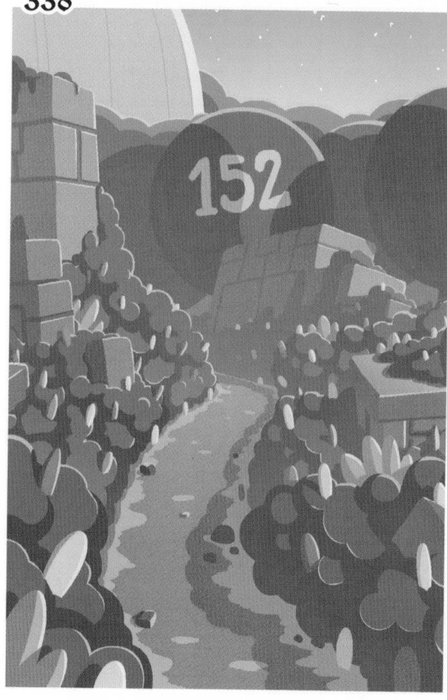
152

339

It's pretty clear you haven't read Pirates: The Great Chase... where you would've already learned this lesson! The ground on panel 229 was cracked and has now crumbled beneath your feet. You're going to die, unless you have more than 15 Agility, in which case you rescue yourself by performing an impressive pirouette landing you at 95. If you die, though, restart your adventure at page 2.

340

DID YOU SERIOUSLY TAKE ME FOR SOME DUMB ISLAND BIRD? YOU CAN TALK TO ME NORMALLY, YOU KNOW!

2
3

A - Why are you completely transformed?

B - Were you affected by the curse at the same time as everyone else?

C - Do you know anything about the curse?

D - You have some magnificent objects in your house. Where are they all from?

E - Did any of the other villagers suffer a full transformation like yours?

F - Do you know Jasmine's secret?

Answers at 203.

341

This ring adds 1 point to each of your Characteristics. You can continue to 274.

342

49

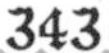

LEAVE ME ALONE, I DON'T WANT TO TALK!
This strange individual won't be answering any questions. You can return to 54.

344

236
304

345

A - Tell me, why doesn't your mother want anyone to enter her home?
B - Who's your dad?
C - Do you sell a lot of weapons in this village?
D - What did you draw?
Answers at 3.

346

87

347

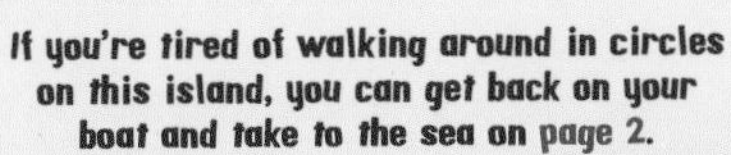
If you're tired of walking around in circles on this island, you can get back on your boat and take to the sea on page 2.

131
35

348

SO, THAT MERCHANT IS RESPONSIBLE FOR ALL OF THIS! ELLIOT, WHO LIVES IN POUSTIFAILLE COUNTY HAS SEVERAL MOONS ON HIS BOAT! FOLLOW ME TO 196.

349

256

350

108

351

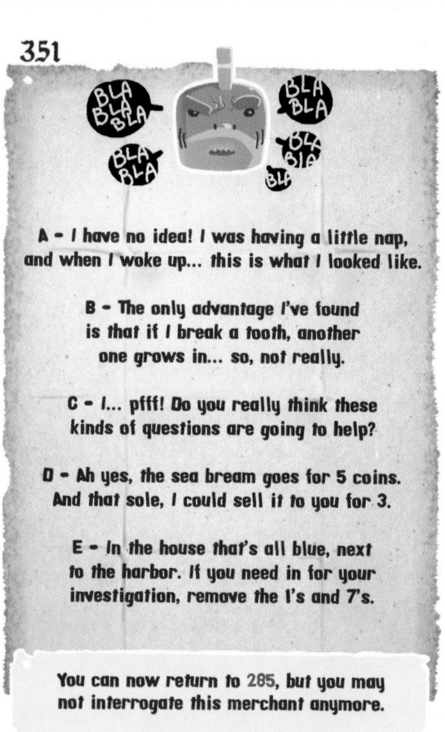

BLA BLA BLA
BLA BLA
BLA BLA
BLA BLA
BLA

A - I have no idea! I was having a little nap, and when I woke up... this is what I looked like.

B - The only advantage I've found is that if I break a tooth, another one grows in... so, not really.

C - I... pfff! Do you really think these kinds of questions are going to help?

D - Ah yes, the sea bream goes for 5 coins. And that sole, I could sell it to you for 3.

E - In the house that's all blue, next to the harbor. If you need in for your investigation, remove the 1's and 7's.

You can now return to 285, but you may not interrogate this merchant anymore.

352

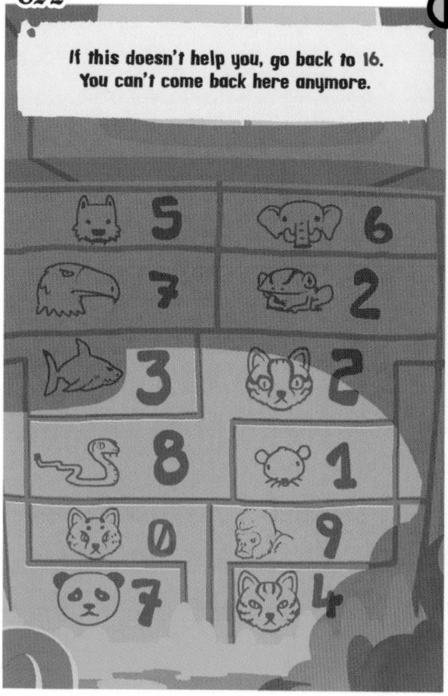

If this doesn't help you, go back to 16. You can't come back here anymore.

5 6
7 2
3 2
8 1
0 9
7 4

353

HMM.. I KNEW SHE WAS HIDING SOMETHING. GO TO THE VILLAGE AND FIND HER, QUICKLY, TO 253.

354

You've been navigating for three days, and you're starting to get hungry! If you don't have a fishing rod, a spear, or a harpoon, you lose 1 Strength point. You decide to set a course to one of the coats of arms you see in front of you, hoping that they're not a result of some sort of sunstroke.

41
232
166
270
334
349
355

355

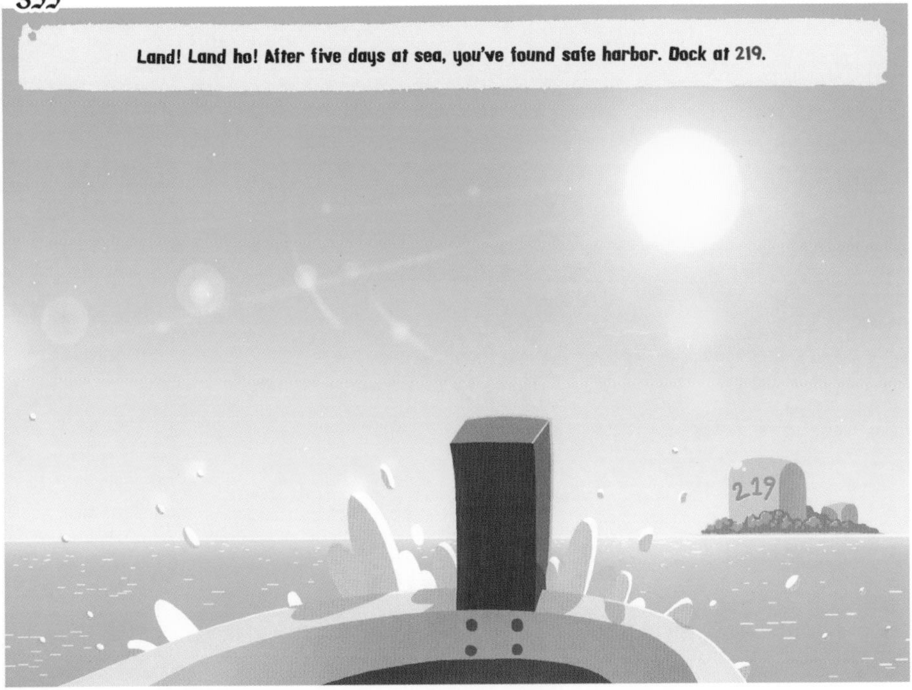

Land! Land ho! After five days at sea, you've found safe harbor. Dock at 219.

219

356

OH, UHH... AH YES, YOU WANT THE REAL RUBY? I DIDN'T UNDERSTAND. PLEASE EXCUSE ME.

I'LL GIVE YOU A LITTLE DISCOUNT, FOR THE TROUBLE. THE RUBY IS 300 GOLD PIECES.

Once you've recovered the real ruby, and spent five days at sea, you dock at Jenova Island. Go to 357.

PIRATE, WE KNEW WE COULD TRUST YOU! YOU LIVED UP TO YOUR REPUTATION, AND THANKS TO YOU, THE CURSE WILL SOON BE OVER. WE CAN'T THANK YOU ENOUGH!

THIS IS FOR YOU, PIRATE! AN AMULET OF KNOWLEDGE. IT WILL BE USEFUL ON YOUR OTHER ADVENTURES.

Pirate, you succeeded in your quest and won everyone's respect.

SPLASH

END

359

WHAT THE HECK IS THIS?

PIRATE, YOU LET YOURSELF BE SWINDLED BY THAT CROOK, ELLIOT! THIS STONE IS NOT THE SACRED RUBY OF THE BURIED CITY!

I'm fairly certain that this is not the outcome you were hoping for. What a fiasco! You've failed and have to restart on page 2.